Iolo's
Revenge

With thanks to Gay Roberts and Norma Allen for recognising the potential in these stories, for making me write them, and for the encouragement of Reginald Massey and Chris Barrett, all of whom I met through PenCambria, our local independent magazine. Thank you also to Wendy Wigley for her wonderful illustrations.

First published in 2018 by Logaston Press
Reprinted 2018, 2019, 2021
The Holme, Church Road, Eardisley HR3 6NJ
www.logastonpress.co.uk
An imprint of Fircone Books Ltd.

ISBN 978-1-910839-24-9

Text copyright © Diana Ashworth, 2018
Chapter illustrations copyright © Wendy Wigley, 2018

Designed and typeset by Richard Wheeler.
Printed and bound in the UK.

Logaston Press is committed to a sustainable future for our business, our readers and our planet. The book in your hands is made from paper certified by the Forest Stewardship Council®.

FSC
MIX
Paper
FSC® C016278

British Library Catalogue in Publishing Data.
A CIP catalogue record for this book is available from the British Library.

Cover photographs copyright © Diana Ashworth.

IOLO'S REVENGE

Sheep Farming by Happy Accident in Mid-Wales

DIANA ASHWORTH

with illustrations by Wendy Wigley

LOGASTON PRESS

for Alan

Put Out to Grass

HIGH in the Trannon valley on the Celtic fringe of the British Isles, where ancient Welsh princes once looked down on the antics of Roman invaders, three of their descendants are fencing a field. All three have shiny new four-wheel drive vehicles. In them, they can bounce over the rough farm tracks, aviate over bumps and splash through fords.

Below them, proceeding slowly up the valley in a very different vehicle, with a following cloud of black smoke, are the couple who have recently bought this land. They are in a small and very ancient, open-topped, three-wheeled dumper truck. It is retired, like themselves, from long public service – in its case from carrying sand and top-dressing at the municipal golf course in the Midlands where their younger son is a groundsman.

They proudly carried it on a borrowed trailer all the way to Wales, rattling and jolting their cautious way through

Warwickshire, Herefordshire and Shropshire. Now, under its own steam – or rather, smoke – it chugs up the winding valley track.

Their dog, of an equally unrecognisable model, bounds ahead of them. As they get to the steep section at the bottom of the meadow where the track peters out, the lady, rotund but still full of the joys of life and second marriage, jumps off to lighten the load and to run along beside the struggling and weighty truck (she feels an empathy with it: it has a low centre of gravity – is stable). As the gradient eases she jumps on again and gives a jolly wave to the fencers.

Now, the rainfall in this part of Britain is prodigious. This meadow holds some of it in an area of boggy ground with reed, marsh orchid and asphodel. Some of it drains through lighter soil and shale to nourish the trees and to gather and erupt from the hillside as mountain springs. These babble down in deep fern edged 'collects', and on really rainy days the surface water joins in to muddy the streams and stain the plaster of the flooded homes lower down the River Severn.

To avoid the marshland and the collects, the retired gentleman and his wife in their retired Cushman dumper truck have to drive to the top of the field where the road, which passed this way in Roman times, would have disappeared up into the forest and where the banks of the ancient track can still be seen.

The fencers are sitting at the field's other top corner having their bait. There is a newly planted hedge where they have been tensioning the new wire fence to keep the sheep from their perpetual duty of deforestation. The couple in the Cushman turn to the left, forced by the terrain to traverse the field at right angles to the steep gradient. The fencers watch – rapt. The couple negotiate the first dip and, as they climb out of it, they start their straight but steeply tilted pass to the workmen. The little wheel at the front of their heavy vehicle has an irresistible urge to travel downhill. The usually disciplined and compliant rear wheels have no alternative but to follow, and the strange green machine turns its own steering wheel towards the valley bottom, and gravity, acting on its great density, does the rest; it gathers speed, confirming the driver's worst fears about the efficiency of the brakes. The fencers rise to their feet and stop chewing. The heavy vehicle is now travelling remarkably fast for such an antique machine. Traversing such long and tussocky grass, it is not bouncing like a four-by-four, but heaving from side to side as if deciding which way to roll. The lady does not wish to be disloyal but thinks of her children, and jumps. Her husband wrestles with the steering wheel a while longer as it lurches to left then to right before himself leaving the vehicle to run alongside, still holding the wheel, still available for crushing or pile-driving into the soft mud of this upland fen.

The dog lies down and passes a front paw over his muzzle as if covering his eyes. Just before the last precipitate descent into the bog there is a slight ridge. With the help of this, the little wheel on the front is at last persuaded to turn, the rear ones concur and the little dumper truck, heavy but stable, comes to a halt, pointing again across the field, albeit in the opposite direction.

The retired gentleman waves in triumph to the watching fencers with the air of someone who has just successfully broken a wild horse. They shake their heads in disbelief and go back to work.

The retired lady picks herself up and rejoins her husband

who chastises her for her lack of moral fibre, bailing out prematurely. She thinks of a cat with nine lives, squeezes his arm affectionately and they decide this will be a very suitable location for loading their new dumper truck with recyclable fence poles, and that they will make their return journey when the fencers have gone home. They walk up the field to the contractors to pass the time of day and have a crack, with all the high spirits of those who have shared a near-death experience.

They had never set out to buy this farm, or indeed any farm. It was a series of casual encounters that had brought them to the area, a place they'd never visited before and of which they knew nothing. There they were one day, sitting on a convenient mossy knoll on the steep hillside in the soft rain, looking down the valley at a cottage-holding about to be auctioned. Now, if you are spiritual or of an anthropomorphic bent, you might think the dilapidated oak-framed building, with water running through the hole in its roof, looked back and said, 'They'll do, they are the ones I want.' Though God only knows why.

They didn't buy at the auction; they didn't even bid. They only went out of respect and interest in the old place. They watched it sold for much more than they could afford and went on their way – but not before shaking the hand of the new owner and wishing him well.

What went on then one does not know. Perhaps the steely cold of the house, damp for so long, made the new owners' breath steam, and the yard-rat ran over the wife's foot and made her quite hysterical. The oak creaked spookily when the wind blew and the electricity went off suddenly. The night outside was starless and blacker than the new owners ever imagined possible, so that they stumbled, disorientated, into puddles; and the screech of the owl and the shriek of the vixen made the new owners' family shudder. To top it all, next morning the well-water in the tap was brown and a toad jumped out of the loo. Anyway, they didn't stay.

The house had asserted itself.

The new owner rang up the retired couple: would they like to buy it? Sadly, the couple explained that he had paid half as much again as they could possibly afford, but they wished him luck in his dilemma. A few days later he telephoned to say he was prepared to accept their offer. 'What offer? You didn't make an offer … Did you?' Of course he didn't. Anyway, that's the way it was: six weeks later, just before Christmas 2005, with the help of their new neighbours, the retired couple were wrestling to get a tarpaulin over the hole in the roof where the sky wept through, rotting the timbers – and the old place seemed to sigh with relief.

Strangely the couple felt they had come home.

The following October the retired lady is chatting to the neighbouring farmer whose sheep have grazed their land all summer and who has been cutting their hedges. His name is Iolo. She is asking about the state of her grass, which is long and clumpy with knots of uneaten hay, while everyone else's grass is as green and tidy as a hilly snooker table with lots of white ovine balls. She asks if it needs topping. Her neighbour says he could top it for her, but she senses that is not what he would do. She asks what else she could do and he answers that he would put a few more sheep on it.

Now, instead of asking when he could bring them over, she hears herself asking how much would ten sheep cost. Sheep prices, it seems, have never been so low, what with the movement restrictions all summer due to the foot-and-mouth. Now farmers are having to sell because of lack of pasture and the cost of winter feed. The lady, temporarily oblivious to the plight of the hill farmer, feels her business acumen (always a problem) stir and almost before she knows it – but she does know it and she knows she will regret it – she does it all the same. She arranges to go with Iolo, a well-respected sheep breeder, to the livestock market the following Monday to acquire ten ewe lambs. This they duly do, and have an all-day breakfast.

They are very fine ewes indeed; just the sort of ewes a cottage holding wants.

On Monday afternoon, when the lady arrives back with the sheep, the couple ask Iolo to leave them in the yard so that they can have a good look at them and make a note of the numbers on their ear tags. They are as big as adult ewes but all fluffy and white with bright eyes and pointed ears. The couple agree that they are not to be considered pretty and will not have names – all the more important to take down their numbers. They find some old hurdles and they drive the hoggs – that's what you call them – into a pen that they have made from the hurdles. And that is when they start to realise just what lively, healthy animals they have procured.

As the lady climbs into the pen to look at the ears, one hogg leaps over a hurdle, and continues to leap with its front feet together like a huge, woolly, gambolling lamb, which of course it is. It gambols straight into the woodshed and to the top of the mountain of precariously piled, as-yet-not-recycled fence posts.

'Mountain sheep', says the retired gentleman. Meanwhile,

the others are taking full advantage of the diversion to jump neatly, one at a time, over the far hurdle and into the hedge beyond. Here they meet a fence along which they file until they find a rotten post which obliges them by lying down and releasing them into the next field.

Time for pragmatism: the nine in the field which is their own are safe so, as a good Christian, the retired gentleman goes for the one soul in peril. He ascends the unstable wood pile and beats the tin roof with a stick until the ewe lamb, who shall be nameless, descends to eventually rejoin her peers, considerably less white and fluffy, and limping pitifully.

'Iolo's revenge', mutters the retired gentleman.

2

The Phantom Tup

THE retired couple had already bought the little hill farm in extraordinary circumstances – not unlike the way they have just bought ten sheep despite being heavily engaged in renovating the tired old buildings for their own occupation. They have spent a night of self-recrimination, general guilt and dreams of RSPCA inspectors; the first day had not proved unreservedly successful. They are now engaged in considerable activity: shifting hurdles, mending fences, building firmer, higher pens where the topography and lie of the hedges would naturally funnel a driven flock. Vaccine and needles, worming and liver fluke medicine are purchased; everything needs to be done in one go. There then ensues an afternoon of fruitless sheep-chasing, stick-waving, gambolling and general falling about, the gentleman on his trusty Cushman – not as manoeuvrable as a quad bike, not quick enough. The lady runs about on foot, up and down the thirty-degree hillside – not as manoeuvrable as a dog, not quick enough.

The old building looks on. The game gets more complex as the ewe lambs – who have spent their lives undisturbed on the moor up to this point – learn the moves. They do this very quickly.

'I thought you said sheep were stupid!' says the retired gentleman as these super-ewes again rotate their platoon commander and try a more sophisticated formation. 'What we need is a dog!'

Their dog is watching from an upstairs window – whining.

Now, the last time the retired lady had felt her heart beating so forcefully against her chest wall was when the fencing contractor had come to look at the job. He had paced the boundaries to be re-fenced, stepping out the hillside in metre-paces, oblivious to the incline or the panting woman at his side. He was in his late-forties, tall, strong, balding and suntanned. She had thought what a novelty it was to see a healthy, mature specimen of the male of the species; that is what had passed through her mind as she had sunk, breathless, onto a convenient ant-hill, saying she would wait for him there. 'Five thousand', he said, and paced on up the hill. She had suddenly realised that everyone she had met for years, however good the grooming or smart the clothes, was out of condition: puny or fat and with the pallor of indoor life, they smoked too much, drank too much and took no exercise. She hadn't realised how bad it had got because it was so long since she had seen anyone healthy.

Her mind having turned from her own pounding heart, she remembers that he had said that, although he had always done a bit of contract fencing and tractor work, he had worked for many years for a local farmer, until the farm had to be sold and he had lost his job. Now he worked for himself all the time, but the lads who helped him (not really lads – one has a teenage son – but young to the retired lady) were really farmers too – not that there is any future in it. One, she feels sure, must have a dog.

The next day, bright and early, the retired lady goes to phone the young man with the dog; but who should she meet on the way but the one healthy man in the British Isles, driving his shiny four-wheel-drive. As is the custom, they stop and chat until another car comes up behind and waits for five minutes. She explains their predicament.

'I have a dog', he says, 'I'll come over in the morning.'

The next day the retired couple are up before dawn, filling syringes and priming their gleaming orange drench gun. Soon there is the sound of a quad bike: it is one of the fencing lads, come up to help. He stands astride his quad like a horseman standing in his stirrups. She opens the gate and he sets off with a roar to bring the sheep down.

Across the fields from the gate lower down a sheep dog is bounding; it shoots past her and up, off, to the sound of the quad and the shouts of the lad. Not far behind comes the older man, striding up the hill, shouting in Welsh to his dog.

'I didn't think he spoke Welsh', says the lady.

'Perhaps the dog does', says her husband.

Seconds later, a small, well-disciplined squadron of proud Welsh sheep – Mountain Division – marches steadily down the hill and, without hesitation, into the pen, followed by a slowly advancing quad bike and one man and his dog. The gate is swiftly closed behind them. The tall healthy man puts a strong arm under the neck of the first ewe and lifts her onto

11

her bottom. The retired lady hands him a syringe of vaccine and he holds it up, like a surgical registrar, in his operating-theatre greens and wellies. He asks exactly what is in the syringe (you wouldn't get that degree of competence in the NHS these days, she thinks) and for an instant the retired lady is a houseman. She tells him the make of vaccine and the expiry date. He smoothly injects it into the ewe's shoulder, then rubs the area. The lad slips the drench gun nozzle down the side of the ewe's mouth and squeezes the trigger, and the young sheep laps the liquid, like an old lady sipping tea. The man reads the number from the ear tag, which the houseman writes down. The lad puts a squirt of orange marker on the back of the ewe's head, like a blessing, and they move on to the next one. In a quarter of an hour they are all dosed and immunised, and She-who-must-be-nameless, still limping slightly, has her shoulders checked and her toe webs sprayed blue.

When the job is done and the gate opened, the dog sends the sheep out, then jumps onto the seat of the quad bike for a stroke and a black-and-white silky, joyful fuss. He was pleased to help and the fencers do not accept any payment.

'What pride there must be', says the retired gentleman, 'in doing a job so well.'

It is the end of November and the weather in Mid-Wales is changing – not just getting colder and wetter, as one might expect, but flinging off its moods one after the other onto the hillside, like a woman with nothing to wear, trying garment after garment, then throwing them with disgust onto the bed: too bright, too frumpy, makes my bum look big … The thick, grey blanket of cloud is drawn slowly over the dark silhouettes of the hills, but there are holes in the blanket and cascades of golden light suddenly tumble from the sky, and for a few minutes the grass has never been greener nor the last oak leaves more gloriously golden.

Then, as a flurry of rain crosses the beams, rainbows appear, taken from a child's view of the world, cut into pieces and stuck on the scene in unlikely places.

Down the valley, the rain is driven from west to east in vertical waves as if the mist has been barcoded.

Now everything that the retired lady turns her hand to has a habit of becoming complicated. True, the actual work is usually done by the retired gentleman, but all the associated negotiations and documentation fill her days. Clearing out a ditch will involve at least three different water authorities, the Welsh Assembly in two languages, the Forestry Commission, an endangered species, a bemused neighbour and a mishap or two along the way.

Keeping sheep is to be no exception despite the small number; it is to be a business, done by the book, each creature enjoying proper attention, at the right time, according to regulations. There are to be no slip-ups this time. Next October, when the ewes are mature, the services of a suitable tup will be employed; a healthy and wholesome ram of the hardy mountain variety, so that the retired couple can increase their breeding stock of hardy Welsh Mountain ewes. Their only worry is that they occasionally have to be away for a day or two; but Jeremy, their neighbour, checks the sheep. He walks up the hill to get a good view. 'Eleven', he says on the telephone, 'but I had had a whisky and they wouldn't stand still while I counted. Oh, and She-who-must-be-nameless is still limping, but less.'

Today the retired lady is finishing her window frames. They have been anti-moulded, protected from tedious and boring insects, base-coated and stained, and are now receiving a layer of varnish to protect against UV (chance would be a fine thing in Wales). She is musing about the safe disposal of her tins when she notices the little flock are grazing, boldly, right outside the large picture-window. She calls her husband to see, and the hoggs (that's what you call them), bless them, turn and walk away. They seem to be rolling their hips in an almost provocative way. They still have the magenta marks on their shoulders that they came with, and each has an orange splodge where they were marked when they were immunised. Now, though, some seem to have a blue smudge on their bottom – the bluer the bottom, the more it seems to be swaying. How odd, thinks the retired lady, it's almost as if a ram with one of those raddle things has mounted them. They get the binoculars and follow them: seven are marked, some quite lightly. 'Looks like he was running out of ink', says the retired gentleman, 'poor old boy.'

'So where is he now, this phantom tup?'

'That's easy', says Jeremy, who has been drawn into the mystery, glass still in hand. 'I saw a Land Rover with a trailer, and I heard some whistling. Didn't think anything of it at the time – I told you there were eleven!'

Next day the retired lady quarters the surrounding hillsides, binoculars in hand. The odd thing is that all the sheep that grazed the surrounding fields a few days earlier are now conspicuously absent. In every direction there are at least two empty fields before she finds any sheep. All the neighbours greet the dog then shake their heads glumly: no one admits to anything; no one uses blue. Iolo's son doesn't think his father even uses a ram; he thinks the vet does something.

'Perhaps I'm using the wrong nomenclature', says the perplexed, retired lady to her husband. 'I was with them when they bought a ram – I mean a tup. Perhaps they call a raddle a ram.'

'It's probably just a conspiracy', says the retired gentleman, 'I wouldn't worry about it – or someone's brought their ram down here every November since time immemorial. It's routine, an ancient tribute, a secret right, a joke, saves us buying a ram, helps us out without insulting us. I like this place.'

The rain stops and the cloud is breaking up, torn asunder with great rents revealing its thick silver-gilt lining and the clear blue sky beyond. The puddles and the wet tarmac and the raindrops clinging to every leaf and rail glisten in the silver light, and great black clouds gather on the western front as the day prepares to fling its party dress onto the wet bracken and don its big black overcoat and matching wellington boots.

3

High-Ho! Farm Electrics

ALL winter, after the apparent but mysterious raddling of her hoggs by the phantom tup, the retired lady scrutinises her little flock for signs of pregnancy.

She can be seen each day, leaning over the gate of the top field, troed-y-rhiw, talking softly to the ten of them in pidgin Welsh. They return her gaze blankly, with the exception of She-who-must-be-nameless who stands apart, bleating a warning to the others.

Climbing the hill every day with a bucket of concentrate does have an advantage. As the grass becomes thinner, the flock (well, 90% of the flock) becomes friendlier. As the retired lady crests the first rise and She-who-must-be-nameless sounds her first alarm, the other creatures scramble to be first at the gate, jostling each other and jumping the collects. 'No good will come of this', bleats the ovine harbinger of doom, as her silly sisters fall over themselves to reach the lady with the bucket.

Obesity aside, there are absolutely no signs of pregnancy, not even phantom pregnancy!

From time to time the retired couple meet the farmers of adjacent land, who ask kindly, albeit with some amusement, after the ewes. They offer ultra-sound.

'No, no! What will be, will be ...'

The ewes, meanwhile, chew the cud wistfully – even virginally. Un-chastened, the retired lady glosses over the dents in her agricultural credibility and moves swiftly on. There are things to be done, trees to plant, Welsh to learn, the farmhouse to finish.

In this inhospitable climate, the first priority should be securing the property against the elements. The wooden back wall of the barn has long ago rotted away, so that the corrugated iron that hangs from its remains flaps in the wind, threatening to fly off in a gale and decapitate any unsuspecting bystander. Fortunately people rarely stand about under these circumstances. However, getting the razor-edged corrugated off the back of the barn and safely stacked in the woodshed is a priority. There it will lie, looking innocent enough, painted as it is with magnolia emulsion, waiting for ankles to sever.

Now, all that separates the barn – which is completely open to the elements – from the cottage parlour is a single sheet of plasterboard. A large tarpaulin (a lorry curtain-side that the retired gentleman always knew would come in useful) is erected to cover the great hole in the back of the barn. It is lashed to the vestiges of the timber frame. The integrity of the barn is re-established.

On this still afternoon the new tarpaulin wall rattles reassuringly and suffuses the barn with a strange blue light.

The retired lady empties the last of the ancient hay from the first-floor hayloft. Her husband, meanwhile, wrestles below with centuries-old oak over the custody of its skirt of galvanised steel as he attempts to demolish the animal stalls on the ground floor.

The hay is eons old and impregnated with a fallen dust of swallow poo and lime mortar that has descended from the inner aspect of the roof slates, where it was applied by farmer and bird alike to keep out the rain. As the retired lady drops arms full of dusty hay from the hayloft window onto the yard below, the dust billows in the shaft of sunlight which illuminates a small area of the loft floor. The deeper layers of hay have twigs mixed in. The more she throws out, the thicker the twigs become. In the shaft of light she spies a really big twig – a small branch really. She pulls and pulls and up it comes with some difficulty, seeming to be stuck under her own feet which she shuffles in order to release it. Up it comes and out of the window with another cloud of dust. Something between her feet catches her eye, a movement – a mouse? She squints down through the iridescent dust. There, between her feet, amidst the filigree tracery of branches beneath her, is the unmistakable form of a be-hatted human head. It is moving about, way down, above the earth of the floor below. It has arms and a crowbar and it is whistling. There is nothing between her and it, nothing apart from sparkling dust and a delicate lace of ancient hazel twigs! She screams and grabs at the timber frame of the hayloft window, easing herself onto it so that she rests like a sack of grain, half in and half out of the window.

'What's up?' says the head as it ascends the ladder and pops up through the hatch. The retired gentleman is not in the least fazed by the sight of his wife's not inconsiderable posterior hung over the sill of the hayloft window, braced in position by white knuckles.

'Stop! Don't come any nearer', she screams.

'Is it a wasp nest?' he asks, 'another dead cat?'

'There's no floor!'

He looks over his glasses at where she has been standing. 'So there isn't', he says. 'That's clever', he says thoughtfully, '… nothing but a felt of criss-crossed twigs holding all that weight of hay for all those years. Look, it's okay if you walk on the rafters,' he says, demonstrating, 'just step from one to the other. Oops, they're not fixed either. Bit wobbly. Second thoughts, hold on to me, we'll get you onto *terra firma* and I'll chuck the rest down to you. We'll have this place stripped in no time.'

And they do. The rafters – modest tree trunks that lay across the timber frame for 150 years – are now piled on top of the corrugated iron, waiting for a new job.

As the blue light of the barn turns to magenta in the setting sun and the dust settles, the couple retire to the parlour. The retired gentleman lights the fire as his wife, coughing, considers the relative probabilities of Farmer's Lung and Psittacosis.

During the night, as the gentleman struggles to turn over under the weight of their three quilts (impeded, as he is, by Long Johns, pyjamas and a tracksuit), he notices that it is raining and that the wind has got up. The blue tarpaulin wall thunders, flinging itself in and out like a great diaphragm as the leaky old lung of a barn sucks air in and out from the blustery night.

The only really tricky thing about a barn conversion, the couple will say in years to come, is floor level: floor level and where that leaves the beam level. You don't want a beam that can't be moved, like the bottom of an A-frame, to be just at head level. The retired couple will eventually always remember this despite their many head injuries from not paying proper attention to it in the first place. Pretty well everything else you can pick up as you go along (easy to say when you have been nursed through the whole process by a team of highly skilled construction psychologists). They are to meet the first two of these today. They are Iestyn the bricklayer (stonemason, master builder and all-round good egg) and Dai the chippy (roofer, tightrope walker and undercover project manager). The two have known each other since childhood but today is the first time they have met the retired couple. They walk around the old barn looking doubtful. There's an awful lot of work here.

'We want to do everything we can, all the labouring and the unskilled stuff', says the retired lady.

The two artisans look even more doubtful.

'There'll be a lot we can't do and you'll have to tell us what we can do, and probably show us', says the retired gentleman, sensing their reticence.

They look at each other for guidance. Rates of pay are discussed and what would be needed: cement mixer, scaffolding … still there is no commitment. The lady makes a list.

'You've stripped out quite a lot already', says one. The couple look pleased.

Starting dates are mooted. An approximate order of work is discussed. Iestyn will present himself in two weeks to lay the footings for the utility room.

Meanwhile the couple are to demolish the old tin lean-to and commission Maldwyn, down the road, and his digger to dig the trenches for the foundations. The retired lady adds various materials to her list. Before they know it, the process seems to have started.

Four weeks later, the architect drops by to see if the couple have talked to any of the local builders yet. The site reminds him of a scene from Walt Disney: there is curling smoke from the bonfire and rabbits bobbing on the drive. The swallows are weaving in and out of the rusty, second-hand scaffolding and the blue tits are fluttering around the crumbs on the sill. There is no roar of power tools, yet everywhere there is activity. A small, round figure in red dungarees and a hard hat is high up on the end gable, hacking out the old pointing with a little pick. She waves to the architect. The cladding from the front of the barn has disappeared, revealing two figures, apparently dancing, with long poles knocking roof tiles off from underneath and dodging to avoid the falling masonry. On the roof of the cottage are two more figures, one sawing, the other hammering. At the front of the house, near the other gable where a garage door used to be, a figure in colourful overalls and a blue hard hat is slapping cement onto a growing wall, laying concrete blocks around the frame of a new front door. The architect, not normally given to humour, cannot resist it …

'High-ho!' he sings in a clear, Welsh tenor voice that rings around the valley. And down they come, their tools slung over their shoulders, singing and whistling. The retired gentleman puts the kettle on and, in the absence of Snow White, recalls that his wife will still be stuck up her wobbly scaffolding tower. Iestyn goes to hold the ladder, steady the tower and

22

avert his eyes as she makes her perilous descent to butter the bara brith and hand out the tea.

The retired gentleman, relishing all this good humoured male company, rebukes Iestyn for letting her down.

Now, unlike the barns, the roof of the adjoining cottage is to be stripped from above, as the existing barge board ceilings are to be retained. To do this, Dai climbs onto the roof. Now it isn't raining, but this is Wales and precipitation can be insidious. Invisible rain can moisten and lubricate every surface, even as the sun shines, nourishing the slimy algae and conducting electricity from wherever it might leak.

Dai does a little skip on the slippery roof. 'I'm getting a bit of a tingle!' says he.

The retired lady is dispatched to check the old fuse board. 'It's all off!'

The retired gentleman double-checks and removes all the fuses, just to be sure.

Dai, however, does another little jump, this time issuing an expletive, and proceeds to do a strange jig, like a cat on a hot roof, down the slippery tiles and onto the wooden platform of the scaffold.

'Farm electrics!' says Iestyn dryly, looking up from the ground and shaking his head; he had known the last tenant.

The following day the electrician arrives with the man summoned from the electricity network provider. The supply to that end of the valley is temporarily disconnected (fortunately they are the end of the line). Every wire leading to the house, barn and outbuildings is disconnected so that every extension lead, hanging loop and dangling recycled junction box is pronounced dead. Ancient ceramic insulators and obscure hanging shapes, wrapped in multicoloured insulation tape, are cautiously removed. The poles carrying the mains supply across the land are inspected for ancient, redundant connections or signs of private enterprise, and all the time the men shake their heads and mumble, 'Farm electrics!'

4

The Wild Men of Dinas Mawddwy

THE cottage holding lies below the ancient earthworks on the hill. It nestles in the gentle valley, where men have lived since time immemorial. Today the house is feeling the chill of the cool, moist air that circulates around its exposed timber frame as it stands in its underwear to be sprayed against beetle and mould. Then it will be re-roofed and re-clad to stand for another century-and-a-half, protecting the folk who tend it and who are, at present, a retired couple who bought it by accident.

Carving his initials in a roof purlin – 'B.J.' – is Bryn the son of Dai the carpenter. He is on work experience from school, and the retired lady has slight misgivings about various health and safety issues. His father is dismissive as he strides along the ridge with nothing between him and the earth floor six metres below, apart from some very puny roof batons which he is about to remove. He was up on roofs like this, helping his father, when he was a lot younger than Bryn.

'Mmm', says the retired lady.

Later that day they are all sitting by the fire having their bait when the lady asks Dai about his father. 'Yes, he was a carpenter and a roofer and, no, he is not alive; he had a nasty accident at work …'

The lady looks enquiringly.

'… He fell off a roof.'

'Ah …' says the retired lady, '… So sorry … I must pop in to town.'

Recently having been electrocuted on their roof, albeit mildly, if it is now to be Dai's destiny to fall from it, they had better be properly insured! She picks up her cheque book and makes haste to the broker.

The retired gentleman very much enjoys the company of the men he calls 'the artisans' (this is to distinguish them from himself, who is the builder's labourer, and his wife, who is the boss). None of these designations hold water as, in times of crisis, which are not infrequent, any one of them might assume control – though usually not the boss. However, the line management created by the retired gentleman allows everyone to take the mickey out of those above them in the pecking order without fear of industrial action or the whiff of bullying. It also adds enormously to the fun of teasing his wife, and encourages others to do so.

Today, however, is serious. They have brought home the new, cast iron wood-burner – not before time as the weather is turning distinctly chilly, and even when barricaded in the parlour they are beginning to feel the absence of most of the roof. They have already excavated the inglenook, removing another dead cat and a shoe for luck. They have to thread the liner down the chimney and blank off the space around it at the bottom; space enough for a man to climb.

'Of course what we really should have are some sickle blades to set, pointing upwards, in the chimney', says Iestyn, who is a stickler for tradition. 'That's what you are supposed to do. You won't have any trouble from the gwylltraid cochion if you do that.'

'Gwitht-what?' asks the retired lady.

'Gwylltraid cochion – the wild men. You know ... The wild men of Dinas Mawddwy. That's right isn't it Dai?'

'And where exactly is Dinas ... what did you call it?'

'Dinas Mawddwy. It's quite a bit further north than here. Red-haired they are, by all accounts.' Then he adds thoughtfully, 'Probably from Ireland originally.'

'And what do they do?' she asks, 'these wild men?'

'They come down the chimney and steal things, and I think there was a murder – can you remember Dai?'

'More than one I think.'

The retired lady looks to her husband for guidance and gets none.

'Iestyn, exactly how long ago was all this?'

'Oh ... Not long.'

'How "not long"?'

'Oh ... Since we've been here – my family that is.'

'About how long, exactly?'

'Only two or three hundred years, perhaps a little longer.'

The retired lady sighs, 'So I don't really have to drop everything and go to Winnstay's for sickle blades.'

'Fair play', says Iestyn, disappointed, 'perhaps not.'

That night they light the wood-burner for the first time and prop sheets of insulation around the parlour. They sit in the glow of the fire. The cat sits on the retired lady's lap having avoided the fate of so many of her ancestors, and the dog lies on a sheet of multi-layered insulating material (£10 per square metre) in the corner of the inglenook. All, it would seem, is right with the world.

On the other side of the thin parlour wall is the eerie blue light of the barn. Scudding black clouds play tricks with the light of the full moon. The blue tarpaulin heaves in and out as the wind builds, and the second tarpaulin, the one laid over the work in progress where the Velux is to go, shifts nervously. This second sheet is held in place, temporarily, by two heavy ridge tiles, sitting astride the ridge with just their weight to trap the plastic of the sheet. New slates have been laid, painstakingly, half-way up the roof and will finally, when they reach the top, be held firm when a whole row of these ridge tiles (they have just enough) are cemented securely into place. Tonight, the ridge tiles are not securely in position. They fidget as the wind lifts the plastic sheet. As the clouds pass in front of the moon their margins gleam silver, then fade as another flurry of great rain drops rattles the roof.

It is at this point that the retired gentleman becomes aware of the developing catastrophe. Having pursued the hot air up to bed at an early hour, they have been sleeping for some time. He is now struggling to find his boots; he has not switched on the light so as not to disturb his sleeping wife. However, she is woken by his loud cursing. Once apprised of the situation, she is keen to join in and soon they both stand in their waterproofs with failing torches and bewildered dog. The plan is for the gentleman, with his superior agility and spatial awareness, to climb up the ladder and through the gap where the landing window will eventually go, thence out onto the scaffold. From there he will climb onto the roof. He will tie the two corners of the sheet, which is flapping like a giant Manta ray, to the scaffolding. He will then edge up to the ridge on his slippery, waterproof bottom, where he will attach the two tow ropes (always useful in an emergency) to the far corners of the floundering fish. He will then throw the other ends of the ropes to his wife who will, by then, be on that side of the building. She will make them secure, thereby fixing the sheet and calming the great sea monster that has landed on their roof. He will then heroically retrieve the precious ridge tiles, of which they have only just enough. He will edge back down the roof with them, so that they will not leap from the ridge and crack the other carefully laid tiles for which they have a duty of care, smashing themselves in the process in an insane, windblown frenzy. All this will be done in intermittent darkness, gusting hurricane winds and driving rain.

To allow his exit through the timber frame at first-floor level (bear in mind they have no floors in this part of the house yet) the rear blue tarpaulin has to be slackened. It flaps hysterically, caught up in the mood, slapping the retired gentleman in the face, wetly. As he tries to squeeze past it, the tow ropes wrapped around his shoulder become caught fast on a nail projecting from the timber frame. With much writhing and a good deal more cursing the nail is prevailed upon to release our hero who emerges uneasily onto the scaffolding. A break in the cloud fills the silver scene with moving shadows and thrashing rain, golden in the torch light. The sky moves vertiginously as the retired gentleman edges slowly up the roof, his wife's pleas for care being carried away by the wind.

As he reaches the ridge they are again plunged into darkness. The retired lady, who is now venturing around the building, falls over a bucket. She wonders how she will find her husband's body when he eventually falls to earth. There is a thud! In the last dying candle power of her tiny torch, the retired lady sees the white triangle on the neck of her brown dog hurtling towards an object on the ground. It is much smaller than her husband. It is a ridge tile tied to the end of a tow rope. She gathers it up and unties the wet rope with difficulty, then pulls on the rope. Guided by fly-away gusts of instruction from above, she ties the end of the rope to the tow bar of the car which is conveniently parked. She was not born yesterday and knows the fallibility of human memory; she takes two half concrete blocks from the pile and wedges them either side of one of the wheels of the car. They repeat the process with the other rope, lowering another ridge tile and this time fixing the rope to a dumpy bag of sand. Then she makes haste around the building and out into the field where the angle will allow her to see the roof. At that moment the moon comes out and she sees the muffled figure of her husband sliding slowly down the newly tiled valley of the roof, onto the scaffold and then disappearing through the hole behind the tarpaulin. She notices that it is flapping less. She looks up at the tilted moon which smiles back at her, roundly. The clouds have gone. The rain has stopped. The wind has dropped. She shrugs her shoulders. 'Wales!' she says.

5

Odd? Not Really

WITH the advent of the retired couple, visitors start to come to the old cottage-holding again. The stout-hearted arrive within weeks to give advice or voice concerns, at least in private, about the mental health of the retired couple who have taken on this massive refurbishment project and 25 acres of farmland. They bring sandwiches but do not stay long – apart from one, that is, older than themselves, who comes again and again, and brings his tools and his blue hard hat.

Once the new roof is on and the wood-burner lit, younger members of the family start to appear with sleeping bags and lovers and trepidation, to see just what the retired couple have got themselves into now.

Neighbours, too, drop in to marvel at the progress, and members of the old family, descended from those who, for over a century, farmed this land. They come to pay their respects to the old place. Tales are told again of when the oaks were felled to make pit-props for the post-war recovery. Remember the piebald horse that kicked the wall of the stable and rattled the china on the dresser? Whatever happened to those horse brasses?

Little by little the retired couple learn the house's history, so that they can look down from Cae Melin and see the new window that looks up the valley, and remember the tale of the time the boys had their pillow fight. So great was the cloud of feathers that billowed from that window that the old man had fancied the house was on fire. My, those boys were a handful. What a thrashing they got that day.

Remember the time one of them threw Nain's best plate from an upstairs window to his brother in the yard: 'Catch!' he shouted (*Duw*, if he had dropped it!) He threw another and another – just asking for trouble. The more the others screamed at him to stop, the more he threw. This old place could tell a tale.

When the couple had first set eyes on the old place, they had peopled it, in the hard times of their imaginations, with old folk, tired from years of toil; with small boys of a lively disposition and with soulful young women. Now, some of them are real and some, grown up, come back to visit. 'Duw', they say as they look at the new kitchen floor.

Today the retired lady is going up to the top field, Troed-y-rhiw, to see about catching the sheep to immunise them; their second jab is due. As she leaves the yard with a hoop of galvanised wire in her hand, the retired gentleman tosses her a strange instrument, a cross between a pair of pliers and a hook-nosed hammer.

'You might find these useful; they are for fencing. Rob gave them to us; he's got a new pair'.

Up in the field she inspects the two old gates that they took up the day before, and looks around for somewhere to build her pen. Considering the number of makeshift sides she has to play with, a corner would be best. The corners of the field are either steeply sloped or fall away alarmingly; one is boggy. There is a place that is flat by the new fence, and there are three trees, small but sturdy. She thinks she could use these as uprights. She cuts back some of the lower branches. The ground between each of the trees is remarkably flat but falls away to form a level bowl in the midst of them. The floor is dry peat and free from vegetation. She kicks away an old, white sheep bone. Now she sets about fixing her two old field gates. She props one in position. It fits exactly, no gap at the bottom, and it fits snugly to the old hawthorn tree, as if the tree had grown with the old gate in position. The other gate is less easy to get into position. She has to cut some more of the lower branches, but it fits. Thus, with the fence, she has three sides of a pen. Now she takes her hoop of wire; she unwinds about a metre and bends it back and fro, to break it. It gets hot but does not break.

'You need a tool', she thinks. She takes out the strange looking pliers and tries them. They cut the wire with ease. She then looks for the best position to circle the hawthorn trunk and fix the old gate. She sees something very odd – well not really, when she thinks about it. There, on the trunk, just about where she will wire her gate, is the ridge in the bark where it was fixed before. She runs her fingers around the bulge where the annulus of wire must have been for years and years. The bark has grown right over it. Sure enough, at one side she can feel a small piece of rusty iron wire protruding from the tree. She winds her wire around the trunk and the

33

upright of the gate and she twists the ends around each other. The wire is thick and her finger begins to bleed.

'Where's your tool?' she glances up and over her shoulder; no one is there.

She gets the tool out of her pocket and looks at it.

'Look at those notches', she hears herself think, 'that's what they're for. Open the pliers and fit the ends into the notches; now close the pliers, careful; now, twist them round. No! – sideways. That's right, see?' The ends of the wire curl neatly around each other, and the gate hutches right up to the old tree trunk. She fixes the other gate, and sure enough she can see exactly where to put the wires from the marks on the hazel tree. Then she thinks about a gate for their new pen. It will need to be about eight-foot, she thinks. She vaguely remembers an old hurdle at the very back of the woodshed. Sure enough it fits exactly. She wires it to the third tree, another hazel with its roots under the fence. The gate swings perfectly.

Later that evening the retired couple shake out a bucket of concentrate onto the floor of the new pen and stand at a distance to watch the sheep jostling to get at it. Even She-who-must-be-nameless, the one suspicious ewe, goes into the pen.

'You've done well', says the retired gentleman, as they stand together admiring the work, his hand on her shoulder. 'To be honest, I didn't think you'd manage it on your own. I thought you'd be down in ten minutes to get me to help.'

'Well, you know, it's odd – although not really, when you think about it – but I didn't feel I was entirely on my own.'

'Mum! There's a weird scratching and rustling in my bedroom.'

'Yes, we noticed that when we slept in there', says the retired lady. Her daughter is up for the weekend. 'It's a mouse.

There's a little hole between the stones up in the corner. When she cleans up she sweeps all the dust out of her hole. That's the rustling – it falls down and makes a little pile on the chest of drawers.'

'Mum! I'm 26. I don't believe in the *Brambly Hedge*.'

'No, really, I'm serious. It needs pointing. And that drumming – it's not your stepfather with a hammer-drill; it's the old woodpecker on the gable end. He makes a terrible din – he's signalling to his mate up the hill. And there's a blackbird that pecks at the kitchen window – the first time I heard it I went out to see who wanted me.'

'This place is scary.'

'No it's not … What's that smell Dear?', says the retired lady, distracted by her daughter's new perfume.

'Jean-Paul Gascony – it's French – do you like it? It's very expensive.'

'Still', answers the retired lady, 'you're getting a lot of smell for your money.'

After lunch the retired lady and her daughter go for a walk. The daughter wants to climb a mountain and call her boyfriend from the top on her mobile. He's Welsh and it will be really cool. They decide to climb Van Hill: not strictly a mountain but quite high enough for a romantic gesture, especially with a retired person with an unruly dog on a string. The retired lady wonders what it is about her daughter that excites the dog so.

It is a beautiful, clear, autumn day and the waters of the Clywedog reservoir are the blue of an Italian lake, though much more beautiful. The sky is clear and the dying bracken is deep red and the tips of the birches are the brightest yellow, like fireworks on the hillside. It certainly is cool. From the top of the hill, surprisingly – though not really, when you think about it – there is a very good signal, and the daughter shouts above the wind to her boyfriend in London that she has climbed her first Welsh mountain. There then ensues a discussion over the airwaves about whose mountains they are anyway.

Mist is lingering in the valleys below the dam, and as they walk through the gorse and heather, back to the track, the shadows are lengthening and the trees seem to stretch themselves across the vivid green sward of the opposite hillside where the sheep graze as sharp points of light, pulling their lines of shadow behind them. At the foot of the hill they leave the sunshine behind, and in this cold vale they speed up. They take a short cut over the meadow that contains horses, eager to get back to the warm.

As they cross the field, the larger of the two horses, grazing peacefully right at the farthest end of the field, sniffs the air. He sniffs it again. He prances like Champion the Wonder Horse – well, not exactly like that innocent hero of early TV. As the horse stands on his hind legs and paws the air with his front legs, the retired lady cannot but notice that he is considerably sexually aroused! He is now heading towards them with a very peculiar five-legged gait. They run.

'Give me the dog, I'm faster!' shouts the daughter as she snatches the lead and accelerates towards the wall. The retired lady puffs along behind – affronted. She is soon overtaken by the crazy horse, still neighing and snorting and tossing his head. You'd think he would trip over himself. Her daughter scrambles over the pile of haphazard rocks that marks the boundary of the field. Daughter and dog continue at speed, in the relative safety of the path that skirts the field, until they exit a more substantial gate, when they stop and look back. All this time the sex-crazed stallion has followed them in the field, circling and prancing and sniffing. The retired lady, confident that she is not the object of his passion, takes her time to negotiate the barbed wire on top of the tumble-down wall, and walks briskly but with dignity to join her daughter.

'Pheromones!' she says crisply. 'What did you say that perfume was called?'

'Jean-Paul Gascony; it's French'.

'You know they make hormone replacement therapy from the urine of pregnant French mares, don't you?' she says to her daughter. 'Well I think we've discovered what they do with the urine of French mares just before they get pregnant!'

As soon as they get home the retired lady sits down to write to *The Times* about the irresponsible use of 'psycho-sexually active fragrances' and their probable connection with increases in promiscuity and sexual crime. It is never published.

Her daughter has a bath and vows never to wear her new French perfume in public again – but she puts it very carefully into her bag for her return to London.

Odd? Not really, when you think about it.

6

Pedro Gonzalez

'P EDRO is a Welsh name – you can see he's a Welsh Hound
 ... Well, predominantly.'

So it is that Pedro Gonzales, Spanish Labrador, formerly of
an indecent number of addresses in Northamptonshire, finds
a place in the heart of Mid-Wales. Prior to this he had been
accepted, and was indeed *en route*, for Wood Green Animal
Sanctuary, that formidable charitable institution where dog-
less people are re-homed with dogs (and indeed a few cats) of
outstanding character.

The problem was that Northamptonshire was simply too
small for a dog of his energy. One decent bound in any direction and he was in the road and someone was bundling him
into a car and taking him to the police station or to their
home to telephone to his then-master. He had been in loads
of houses and most of the cars in the district; he knew the
routine and he knew all the policemen.

Sometimes, when he was bored, he would let himself out and go down to the dog pound to see who was there, and to lick the fingers of the custody sergeant to see what he had had for lunch.

Every time he had to be collected there would be threats and recriminations from his then-owner. Some people, Pedro had learned, just can't tolerate not being the main mover in a relationship, and just hate not being as well-known as their dog.

'Okay Pedro', said his then-master, 'you can have 24 hours with this couple. They're moving to Wales and they're mad enough to have you, but if you don't cut the mustard then it's off to Wood Green with you'.

'Fair play', said Pedro, which was a sign.

'That poor dog needs some exercise', said the retired lady as she got out her bike and wheeled it out onto the bridle path that ran behind their previous home.

That day they – she and Pedro – cycled across the fields to the disused railway track (now a long distance cycle track) and then all the way to Market Harborough and back. It was 25 miles for a not especially fit lady on a bike, and at least three times that distance for a Welsh Hound, quartering the ground as he went, leaping over fences and exploring under all the bridges. That evening, for the first time in his life, Pedro Gonzalez felt settled. He had his tea and lay down on the rug between the retired lady and the retired gentleman and snoozed. He felt no need to restlessly sniff the air that came in under the door, to chew chair legs or jump on people's laps, or even chase the cat up the curtains. When someone came in he didn't bound past and off, up to the take-away, to put his feet on the counter and lick the lady's face. He just opened one eye and closed it again. They had cracked it: 75 miles a day and this dog was fine – or rather these 'owners' were fine. So it was decided that Pedro would move to Wales.

Pedro is not a fully qualified sheepdog yet. The retired couple think it safer to discourage social interaction with sheep at this stage. He is an intelligent and urbane creature, a theatre lover, regularly attending the open-air performances in the botanical gardens in Sheffield. He has seen Hamlet, but best of all he likes Oscar Wilde – such formidable female characters. He sits to attention, ears akimbo whenever Lady Windermere is centre stage (you know where you are with those sorts of people).

He thinks that there are far more of his type of people in Wales.

'What a friendly dog', they say as they bend down to let him sniff them.

There is none of this does-he-bite-will-he-jump-up-oh-he's-muddy business that one gets in the city. Farmers look at him appraisingly and say, 'That's a very powerful dog'. What they mean, the retired couple do understand, is: 'That's the sort of dog that could kill a sheep in a trice.'

He's not at all interested in sheep, they explain, much more interested in other dogs and sticks: he is an obsessive retriever. Pedro has a particular penchant for those polystyrene tubes which come from the builder's merchant primed with silicone gel, adhesive, putty and all other gooey substances destined to be injected into buildings that you are renovating. When empty, these are discarded. Pedro brings them back. They are discarded once more. You can follow the drift.

This gets tiresome after a time, so Iestyn weights the tube with stones and some mortar; then he can lob it right over the stream. By the time Pedro returns with his tube, Iestyn is up the scaffold. A ramp is quickly manufactured, one which a dog can safely charge up and down with a tube in his mouth. So quick is the dog that it is not infrequent that he arrives at his projected destination before the tube which then cracks him on the head.

'Hard hat area!' says the health and safety officer. Without malice, Pedro carries it back and lets it drop, plop, into the mason's mortar.

Dai, the carpenter, has a different technique: he rams an off-cut of roof batten into another tube. He throws it over and over again. When he gets bored, he hides it. He hides it more and more cleverly and inaccessibly. Sometimes, hours after Dai has gone home, the retired gentleman has to get a ladder out and go to help the dog find his precious tube so that they can all go to bed.

Thus the tradesmen who work on the house, doing the things the retired couple cannot do, are paid by the hour, which includes approximately 15% TTT (or Tube Throwing Time). Unlike VAT, it is in no way reclaimable; it is just another of those insidious on-costs.

The truth is, if tube throwers are distracted, Pedro is not without his own resources. He will saunter casually up the lane until he is out of sight, glancing furtively over his shoulder. Once around the bend, he puts his head down and his ears back and he's off!

Pedro, with his cheerful disposition and distinct markings, is an object lesson in how difficult it is to disappear in rural Wales. Movements up and down the roads that lead up onto the moor may not be frequent, but as each vehicle passes another they stop and exchange news. This infallible network will relay tidings of fallen stock, road kills, heart attacks, infidelity and unaccompanied canine movements in less time than it takes to log on to the internet.

The postman reports that there have been sightings three miles down the valley at the home of Mrs Jones, whose bitch is in season. When the retired lady drives into Mrs Jones' yard there are no other vehicles around. Pedro, who is standing on the diesel tank striking a very debonair pose, jumps down with a certain swagger: 'Must be off – my driver's here.'

He jumps immediately into the open door of the still-moving car. The retired lady turns it around as quickly as possible; the door slams closed and she beats a rapid retreat, wheels spinning on the gravel. Pedro, standing on the back seat, wags his tail and tosses his head in farewell to the two enthusiastic bitches chained to their kennels. The retired lady feels like an accessory after the fact. At any moment the contents of a bucket of water might be heading her way.

Ten weeks later the retired lady casually asks the postman if there are any puppies in the valley. None that he is aware of. She sighs a great sigh of relief and bustles off to find the retired gentleman to impart the good news. She is distracted by the sound of excited shouting and barking from the opposite side of the valley, near where the public footpath goes through the woods.

'Oh no! Where is he?'

Seeing that Pedro is not in the yard, she hurtles down the path to the river: sure enough, there is a strange car parked in the lay-by. She runs up into the wood where she finds a very large, red-faced and angry man staggering under the weight of a large and aged bitch, held in his arms like a huge, ungainly baby. Around him, as he staggers down the path back towards the lay-by, dances a very fine but bemused ginger and white Spanish Labrador.

'Is she okay? Can I be of assistance?' yelps Pedro, playfully. The bitch is turning her head from side to side, struggling to see this charming cur, and is proving difficult to carry. A well-dressed lady is following with another dog on a lead. She is berating the red-faced, angry man.

'I told you she was coming into season, but oh no!' she says, nodding to the retired lady who now has Pedro under control and attached to her belt (which she had removed with great alacrity), 'you know best.'

The retired lady apologises profusely. The man staggers on purposefully, exchanging bitter recriminations over his shoulder with his wife, who turns and shrugs helplessly at the retired lady and Pedro.

They think it best not to follow, but wait in the woods until they hear the unfamiliar car leave the lay-by.

Pedro's absences are becoming more frequent and worrying, though always predictable. Pedro is in love. If those appointed to keep him out of trouble waver for an instant in their diligence – to put out a vomiting cat or to look up at the red kites stacked in the blue sky above the old cottage-holding – he will abscond. Before the cat has run around the house and in the cat-flap to resume her retching, he is halfway down the valley. Cunningly, he now avoids the postman by making straight for the river and then, in the cover of its banks, so that even the sheep do not give away his position, he trots, dapper and debonair, to where the ditch from the side of the old church drains into the river. Here he pops up and never fails to fain surprise and pleasure at meeting a retired person, wearing a long-suffering glare and carrying a lead which is slipped on as he is led away.

'Poor old boy!' says Brian, looking over his garden fence (he knows a good dog when he sees one).

The object of Pedro's affection is a beautiful and lively Old English Sheepdog (we'll call her Jade to protect her reputation). She lives very near to Brian in a house with a magnificent landscaped garden. It has little river-stone walls with plinths for stone statues, and ornamental pots overflowing with verdure. They are ideal for scent-marking. At these times Jade luxuriates, most of the time, in a large double-glazed conservatory overlooking farmland, hermetically sealed, so virtually 'invisible' to Pedro, who sees mainly with his nose. However, when the door of the conservatory is opened to the garden, she bursts forth into his consciousness. The essence of her surges up the valley, under the door, through the keyhole and in through the cat-flap.

On the one occasion that he makes it, undetected, all the way to her garden, she is already back in her crystal cage; but he busies himself in an ecstasy of doggy aroma, replying to each of her invisible messages with robust and eloquent ones of his own. Pale green trickles anoint every pot, and meander down the plinth of the bird-bath. The lower panes of the French windows and of the conservatory are systematically sprayed, and little piles of something very smelly are carefully balanced on all the little statues.

There! ... Pedro surveys his handiwork with pride, just as the retired lady comes puffing across the footbridge and, at the very same moment, Jade's owner opens the front door. As

Pedro is shackled and dragged from the scene, the man looks bewildered at his violated Eden.

'So terribly sorry', says the lady, who has taken in the scene. She tightens her belt around the dog's throat so that his eyes bulge – not unlike the man's as his eyes move from pot to pot and onto a little stone statue with its crowning glory …

'Is your dog ill?' he asks.

'Not yet …'

And nothing could be nearer the truth. Pedro is grounded for the next three weeks. Each time the door of the conservatory down the valley is opened, a waft of something so irresistible spreads up the valley that Pedro shivers and pines and howls and claws at the doors. Towards the end of the three weeks he has wilted; he is thin, subdued and tremulous from the constant state of nervous arousal. As this surge of terrible passion wanes, the retired couple, equally exhausted, secure the dog in the cottage and join their very good neighbours for an evening meal.

After three courses and a bottle or so of wine, there is a knock at the door. It is Brian from down the valley. He is looking for the retired couple who, as we know, are not at home. He has their dog, who was causing a bit of a din at his neighbours' house. Fortunately, they too are out.

Pedro is repatriated and the cottage is examined. A small upstairs window, the flap at the top, has been forced open from the inside, probably not more than 16 feet from the ground. Otherwise the house is still completely sealed.

'Poor old man!' says Brian.

7

Lumberjacks and Backwoodsmen

WHEN the retired couple happened upon the 25-acre cottage-holding in 2005, they had had no plan to buy it or to move to Wales. They had no desire to brave the elements or to test themselves, physically and mentally, every day of their lives. It had just all happened. From orderly, deliberate lives they had fallen, without realising it, into One-thing-leads-to-another-and-before-you-know-it-Land.

They don't even remember how they got into forestry. They must have done something to attract the attention of the Forestry Commission. Now they spend happy hours drinking tea and eating bara brith with the young forestry advisor who admits to only modest up-take of his woodland schemes this year. The retired couple suspect they are his only clients and, it turns out, his Dad used to play cricket with the retired gentleman. Farmers, he observes sadly, are generally not enthusiastic about giving up grazing land. The retired lady voices her doubts about how they will ever manage to harvest their proposed crop of oak.

'You don't have to worry about that,' says the young man kindly, 'you'll be dead … Someone else will sort it out.' She is reassured. The current schemes finish at the end of the following month; next year's one will be considerably less generous, but if they get a move on they can get it all signed up before the end of the tree-growing year. And they will be eligible for more than double the standard grant as there is definite evidence that this land was wooded in the past and adjoins the remains of other ancient woods. The thought of replanting an ancient woodland appeals. And they are eligible for the Farm Woodland Premium Scheme!

'That's good … What exactly is that?'

'That's compensation for loss of grazing and the reduction in your Single Farm Payment.'

'Oh yes … Single Farm Payment … I don't think we've got one of those.'

'Of course you have. It comes in December … You have got a Holding Number, haven't you? – A Holding Number is key to everything in Rural Payments. Without a Holding Number we are done for. You'll have to get one issued as soon as possible; you'll have to go to the Welsh Assembly offices … There is still time …' Suddenly the retired couple see something new in the eyes of Robbie, the woodland advisor. It is a sort of heroism – Dunkirk spirit. They have six weeks; they can do this thing!

Thus opens another whole avenue of experience, previously unknown though not entirely unfamiliar to the retired couple. They are starting to understand what drives the farming year, what furrows the brows of their neighbours: not the seasons nor even the weather but the grinding bureaucracy of the Welsh Assembly Government and the EU!

The following day, having ploughed the internet over-night, the retired lady makes her way to Welshpool Livestock Market to talk to the local Welsh Assembly Farming Advisor. Do you know that for every farmer working the land there are 56 allied professionals skimming off their share of the farmer's profit? This the retired lady learns from Iolo, whom she meets in the car park ('allied professionals' was not the exact term he used). From vets to fertiliser salesmen, advisors, inspectors, clerks, land agents, interpreters, IT specialists, shag-pile carpet salesmen in Aberystwyth and purveyors of prawn sandwiches for working lunches in Cardiff – all, according to Iolo, take their pound of flesh from the carcass borne on the back of the Welsh hill-farmer.

Mrs Higginbotham is very helpful. Being of a certain age herself, she quite understands that the retired lady needs to take copious notes. She gives her myriad leaflets and thinks it only fair to point out that their last opportunity to purchase entitlements will be at the auction in Welshpool, the day after tomorrow. It seems that, in order to appear on the radar of the Welsh Assembly (Rural Payments Wales), one not only needs to have agricultural land and a holding number, but also bonds, called entitlements, which can be traded and which entitle you to a share from the agricultural pot (after the shag-pile carpet salesman in Aber and the sandwich man in Cardiff and all the others have had their cut). The size of this pot is variable, so the value of the investment is impossible to assess and there are plans afoot to change it all anyway; but you can be sure it will be replaced by something similar.

This latter information is acquired from the sensible young woman at the land agents the following day.

'She's nice', says the retired gentleman, as she goes out to get the forms, 'do you think she'd be interested in marrying our eldest son?'

'Shh!'

On the Monday following, three large manila envelopes protrude from the letter box: one has already broken down under the strain of the paperwork; two are from the Assembly and contain forms and books of regulations and notes on filling in forms and coding land-use and assessing soil erosion and nitrogen usage and regulations for ear-tagging – all of which are impossible to understand. The third is confirmation that the couple own 4.7 entitlements at a total cost of £940.

'When did you say we'd break even?' asks the retired gentleman.

'Not sure – but there'll be hidden benefits and tax advantages.'

'We hardly pay any tax.'

'You'll be able to claim for things like a new chainsaw. It'll help pay for the accountant …'

'We don't have an accountant.'

'We'll have to get one! We'll need advice about tax returns, auditing partnership accounts …'

The retired gentleman cups his head in his hands.

'Last year was the first in 40 years that I didn't have to fill in a tax return. What have you done? … Did you say I could claim for a new chainsaw?'

The new chainsaw has the longest jib the retired gentleman

can comfortably handle. It is twice the size of the one he bought when his life was last in crisis, just after his previous wife had inexplicably departed. It is easy to start. Today they are cutting down a dead tree that threatens to fall across the footpath and bring down the fence. It is a Saturday, so Jeremy, their neighbour, is helping; but the combined pulling power of Jeremy, in his lumberjack shirt, and the retired lady is insufficient, as the trunk has saved itself in the arms of a neighbouring tree.

'There's nothing for it: that bough will have to come off too.' They reposition the ladder and they scan the surrounding treetops for signs of electricity wires. They don't want a repeat of the Bank Holiday fiasco, when they cut off the electricity to 3,000 houses (that was in the Midlands). It wouldn't have been so bad if it hadn't been just before lunch.

'All clear!' There is a growling from the saw and a blizzard of wood chippings and sawdust. There is a mighty crack as the bough breaks, relinquishing its grip on the dead tree, which crashes to the ground and bounces on the forest floor – such power!

Next, it is cut into 'manageable' lengths – but not before the new saw jams, so they manoeuvre it to the water's edge in an 'unmanageable' length, which they roll with levers and haul with ropes into the stream. Now, with Jeremy and the retired lady heaving on tow ropes – one on either side of the stream like barge horses (though less serene), and with the retired gentleman in his waders pushing from behind, and a lot of shouting and splashing – the trunk is transported downstream. Here the Cushman, their homicidal, three-wheeled dumper-truck, waits in the field. Thence, the great oak trunk is towed to the yard where it will remain. As it is pulled across the slope it rolls on its rope, back towards the river. The retired lady intuitively jumps and the rope passes beneath her (no skill is ever wasted – not even skipping).

With each rotation of the trunk the Cushman stamps its back wheels on the ground, but today it cannot quite get the impetus to flip over. Today it does not fling off the yolk of slavery or the retired gentleman, but angry smoke billows from the vents by the engine, leaving no doubt about its true intent.

At the end of the exercise, they are all wet and cold and covered in wood chippings, but they are all definitely alive – although the next morning they will not be quite so sure.

The new trees are planted in February, with minus seven degrees of frost. Robbie explains that they could do it themselves, but strongly advises that they do not. Reluctantly, they employ a contractor. He is a young man of about 30, working with his father who wears a beaver hat and a walrus moustache. George plants the saplings, of which there are more than 7,500. He makes a V-shaped cut in the turf and slides each in, two metres apart. He trudges slowly across the hillside, his father a few trees behind, putting in the canes and slipping over the clear plastic cylinders to keep off the rabbits. They work silently and gradually, back and forth across the hillside, keeping up the steady plod for hour after hour, punctuating the landscape with thousands of broad-leaf saplings, planted as nature would. The oak take pride of place, as they will become dominant, interspersed with rowan. Hazel is planted around the edges with the aspen and alder in the wet flushes. They plant the holly in thickets from which they can extend as an under-growth. The wild cherry trees are grouped in prominent places, to make a show and fruit better for the birds. Nothing escapes the tree-planters notice. As the frost gives way to torrential rain and the retired lady arrives with tea, they point out the areas where they suspect there are lead deposits – there are no worms in those areas. Each day she swaps cups of tea for pearls of arboreal wisdom as she learns how important the native trees and plants were to our most distant ancestors.

Meanwhile, the young man's immediate ancestor's cough is deteriorating day by day. Doesn't he think a few days in the warm might be a good idea? He does not. And who is to argue with a man who still regularly goes off into the wilderness of his native Canada, or up into the hills of Britain, with his Welsh-speaking son, to live off the land?

Back in the relatively warm kitchen of the cottage the radio is talking about a climate change conference somewhere exotic. Britain's representative, about to set off to it by plane, assures the listener that his attendance will be carbon neutral: they have planted an astronomical number of trees to offset the air travel. It dawns upon the listener that these trees almost certainly include the exact same ones that George and his father are, at this very moment, planting, and which will ease their consciences on their next trip to Canada. The listener wonders how many other people in the chain of events that culminates in the planting of a tree will claim the ecological kudos.

As if to emphasise the folly of any man claiming responsibility for growing trees, a very strange thing now happens. It stops raining. The sun comes out and there follows the hottest, driest spring since records began in this part of Wales (when Colin, down the valley, got his mini-weather station).

It does not rain again until May, by which time nearly all the aspens are dead (that is all the aspen they planted). A year later the retired couple notice that in the poorest areas of this land, where the soil is thinnest and where George had seen no point in planting anything, the ground is shimmering with the quaking, shivering leaves of self-sown aspen!

8

Reflections on Language

I N another life the retired lady had spent a lot of her time trying to explain things to elderly ladies who did not speak her language. She had always suspected that interpreters, particularly sons-in-law and landlords, could not be trusted, and that, 'You need to rest that back/ shoulder/ voice', became, in translation, 'It is important to keep active/ work in the shop/ deal with all the calls from home.'

'Would you like me to talk to the housing department?' became: 'This nice man here will find you somewhere to live, and look after all the paperwork and money.'

The gist of the above conversations was deduced by the retired lady simply by the power of non-verbal perception. She spoke no Somali (if that was what it was), nor Yiddish, nor Gujarati, nor Urdu – not even a smattering of Swahili. For this reason, she was an enthusiastic hander-out of flyers for English classes; she had drawers full, in all the different scripts and tongues, now carefully segregated from the fam-ily-planning leaflets which she also slipped into shopping bags.

For this reason, when they eventually move to Wales and someone hands her a flyer about learning Welsh and mak-ing new friends and becoming integrated within a welcoming culture, she knows she has to do it.

She chooses a class for parents and grandparents (her demographic), to help them support their children and grandchildren learning Welsh (she has not got a child to sup-port but will find one later). The whole ethos of the course is foolish, as everyone knows that the language that children speak is completely different from that of their parents and grandparents.

For two years she learns the proper, grammatical language; but, when people speak to her in Welsh, their expectant looks are met with blank bewilderment. Even Derek, the friendly television weatherman who always gives a little greeting in the local vernacular, seems foreign to her. He never says the, 'How do you do?' and the, 'Good morning Mrs Jones', that she learns in her class.

She learns the fiendish nature of the complicated gram-mar of an essentially simple language ('a simple language for simple people', says Iestyn) that mutates its words according to what they are doing by changing their first letter. It can do this in lots of different ways depending on the gender of the word described or its tense or who owns it or its posi-tion relative to the speaker. A place you've been will have a different name if you are going to it. Can you imagine, if it were English? – It would be something like: this is a creature; this is one greature; this is my ngheature (does the prickly moniker begin with 'c', 'g' or 'ngh'?) Welsh is like this, only much more complicated ... so let's call them hedgehogs, as words beginning with 'H' don't mutate!

Thus, a simple rustic vocabulary becomes impossible to look up, as a word can begin with any of several letters. The retired lady is nothing if not a willing student and she learns all the rules of mutation and conjugation and she reads all the road signs aloud as they go along, which is very irritating. Saying anything involves verbal calculations equivalent to a super-killer-Sudoku and takes equivalent time. Conversation moves on and the moment is lost.

The inspector visits their class and, after the mandatory eating of cake, questions the students in Welsh about their progress. There is a long silence. The inspector looks enquiringly at the teacher: 'It's alright', she says, 'they are old – it takes time.'

Just saying 'Yes' and 'No' is a dilemma. If a Welshman asks, 'Are you well?' you can't say, 'Yes, thank you!' You have to say, 'I am, thank you!'

'Did you enjoy the show?' requires the affirmative, 'I did.'

The kind enquiry: 'Would you like a banana/ one ganana/ a bite of my vnhana?' can't be accepted with a, 'Yes, please!' You have to say, 'I would, please!' or decline with, 'I would not.' Thus there are as many ways of saying 'yes' and 'no' as there are things to do and times to do them – but only one is right. This, the retired lady begins to suspect, might explain the charming lack of dogmatism in the national stereotype. No one ever really wants to make a hard and fast (yes or no) decision, even in English.

She knows native Welsh speakers find this difficult, and grandparents constantly complain that their grandchildren don't even know how to say 'yes' and 'no' properly in their mother tongue.

Now, there is another complication with Welsh, and that is the constant urge that its speakers have to abbreviate it. Machynlleth becomes 'Mach'; Llandrindod Wells becomes 'Llandod'. Verbs seem particularly prone to shortening, with letters vanishing and perhaps a syllable disappearing every generation. The Welsh worry about the loss of their language due to immigration, dilution and intermarriage but, the retired lady thinks, there may be equal threat from constantly mislaying bits of it. One day it will be replaced by one huge apostrophe.

Living in a bilingual country and chatting with grannies is throwing up fascinating conundrums. The retired lady has spotted that language might be strangely connected with gender identity. Linguistically mixed marriages are common. Language is just one of those differences that human nature finds sexually attractive. In such marriages there is usually the will to pass on both languages, so each parent will speak their mother tongue to the children. Little boys growing up speaking Welsh to their dads and English with their mums are bound to marry English-speaking girls – or so their grannies say. Similarly, boys who speak to their mums in Welsh and their dads in English will assiduously seek out a Welsh-speaking girl to marry – or so the theory goes.

Boys and girls who speak Welsh at home and learn English properly (like smoking only when they go to high school) will associate the language with adulthood – a sort of linguistic puberty. This explains the grandfather who will chat to his grandchildren in Welsh but only address his grown-up sons in English.

Long-standing relationships can, the retired lady fears, be destabilised when the English-speaking partner decides at last to make a monumental effort to learn their partner's language, and wants to practice with them for a few minutes every day. If her theory is correct, it is like a wife or girlfriend saying, 'I want to understand your maleness better, so I've started boy-lessons and I want you to treat me like a man for half an hour every evening and for ten minutes before we go to sleep.' It won't work!

Although, after several years, the lady can explain the syntax of all the road signs (which makes her husband sigh) she becomes a rabbit in the headlights when addressed in Welsh. Her friends say, 'Come with us – it's fun. He's really young and it's not like work at all; he doesn't worry about grammar, and Mary brings a different homemade cake every week.' And so the retired lady starts another Welsh Class – conversational – contemporary – abbreviated – carbohydrate-reinforced.

'S'mae!' says the teacher. That's what Derek the friendly weatherman says!

'S'mae!' says the retired lady without thinking.

9

Beginner's Luck

WHEN the retired couple bought the cottage-holding it comprised a basic, two-bedroom, timber-framed cottage with adjoining barn. The rear, west-facing, wall of the cottage and the gables were of sturdy stone with an inglenook fireplace and large bread oven. Three-quarters of the rear of the barn was also stone. The front wall of the cottage was timber-framed, the original lath-and-plaster infill having been replaced by a jigsaw of single bricks roughly mortared into place, with large gaps where only the outside render and the inside plaster kept out the weather.

The human accommodation was basic; the original earth and pitching floor (pebbles laid on edge, sitting on the earth) had been thinly skimmed with concrete and quarry tiled. Rats burrowed beneath the floor, emerging from a small volcano in the earth floor of the cupboard-under-the-stairs. The retired couple had taken it for a molehill initially (that was bad enough!) So thin was the floor that lighting a fire produced condensation under foot – a heavy dew.

The timber frame of the barn was clad with tarred larch planks, warped for ventilation. The rear cladding, which faced the horizontal rain from the west, had long rotted away. In the 1980s an extension had been added providing a rather incongruous and suburban integral garage, too small for any self-respecting farm vehicle. Above it was a third bedroom and a bathroom with hot water from the Rayburn in the kitchen. The acid water from the well turned rust-coloured in the cast iron boiler, so that one's extremities disappeared into russet oblivion at bath time. In truth, the necessity of removing all one's clothes simultaneously in order to immerse oneself in four inches of rusty water must have been unthinkable in the winter months.

The barn was divided into bays: one was a stable, one was a llawr or 'floor' on which was stored those things that had to be kept dry. Here, whole oak tree-trunks lay on the earth, the upper and lower sides squared off, supporting a floor of thick oak planks, held in place by great wooden dowels. The last two bays were for the milking cows and, finally, the pig. A little door, less than a metre high, was provided in the end gable for the pig's convenience. That is how it was: approximately four times the accommodation for the horse, the two cows, the pig and the winter feed as there was for the family of twelve and the lodger!

Sheep lived outside. There was, and still is, a separate lambing shed of a more primitive though younger construction. It is a cunning mélange of timber, corrugated iron and plastic with tarpaulins, frayed to attractive green and blue fringes, and sheets of disparate material from feed-bags to bits of Morris Marina. It was a traditional farm outbuilding, all held together with baler twine.

Times have changed. Human needs now predominate. The old barn has seen its stable and llawr turned into a living room; the great oak boards replaced by inches of brittle plastic insulation, set in concrete and veneered with flooring made from inferior French oak, which curls when it is left out in the rain. The old beams creak their disapproval in the warm, dry air. There is a fitted kitchen where the cows chewed the cud, and a new-fangled wet-room where the old sow snored.

Now that the retired couple face their first lambing season, the lambing shed, in all its aforementioned glory, is full of building materials and salvaged timber.

They clear a small area and fence it off with pallets and baler twine, just in case of emergencies. The plan is to lamb their little flock out of doors; they are a hardy breed and there will be less chance of infection. Not easily being able to catch them is another factor! They are, however, painstakingly manoeuvred into the field nearest the house, and the retired lady acquires a powerful torch. It is cold and they are being fed twice a day.

Two weeks before the earliest possible date of lambing there is a funeral in the Midlands. They decide to risk it and go. Jeremy, their neighbour, and his good wife are briefed. The torch is handed over. No sooner is their dear friend laid to rest than the mobile phone rings. It is Jeremy. One ewe has taken herself off from the flock. The retired couple are not sure how significant this might be; they hum and ha in a panicky sort of way, then they set off for home. Jeremy's wife phones: she thinks something is hanging, membrane-like, from the ewe's behind. The retired couple break the speed limit through Spaghetti Junction. They hammer up the M54. At Shrewsbury the lamb is still not delivered and the cat, who travels with the retired couple, howls with discomfort at the speed at which they take the roundabouts on the ring road. By Newtown the ewe is definitely restless and Jeremy's wife wonders if she is in discomfort. As they turn up the valley at Trefeglwys the ewe is reported to be restive and pacing up and down by the hedge. They splash through the puddles along their track to the gate where Jeremy and his wife stand, still in pyjamas, wellies and anoraks. They had only popped out to feed the chickens. The latest progress report is given: there is no progress – the ewe looks plaintively at the retired couple. Jeremy and his wife withdraw to get dressed and warm their blue extremities. They pass the car abandoned on the track: the dog is sitting upright in the driver's seat, front paws resting on the steering wheel, eyes fixed on the road ahead. The cat is retching on the parcel shelf.

The retired couple look at the ewe; they look at each other. The retired lady goes to put on her waterproof trousers, and fetches her pre-prepared obstetric bucket with all the bits and pieces in, and a warm towel from the airing cupboard (optional extra). They approach the creature tentatively; she moves away. They follow; she starts to run. They regroup to consider – what on earth do they do now?

At that moment there is a strange sound, like a chainsaw. No, it's not a chainsaw. It is a guardian angel; not a Hells Angel on a motorbike, but Rhodri on his quad bike. They watch him drive around the lane that skirts the field, then up the track and right into the field, standing in his stirrups.

'A'right?' he asks, looking down at the ewe who is straining again. 'That's not right. Shall I have a look?' With that, as the ewe crouches again to strain, Rhodri confidently takes hold of her front end as the retired lady takes the rear end. Thus, they frogmarch her to a little fenced-off pen by the gate, then roll her gently onto her side in the mud. She does not resist. A few seconds later Rhodri has pulled out a lamb. It is large and floppy and covered in khaki coloured slime. It is hardly breathing but, unlike its twin, which Rhodri is now extracting, the first one is alive. Rhodri does all the things that you are supposed to do to put breath into the little lifeless lamb – all to no avail. The second, premature twin, a ram lamb has perished.

They hold the surviving, flaccid, slippery creature to its mother's teat. It cannot suck; it cannot stand. Heavy rain is now drumming around them. The retired and deflated lady wraps the lamb in the damp towel and, thanking Rhodri from the bottom of her heart, takes it to the house. The retired gentleman passes her. He has found two old doors and a pallet, and will make a shelter in the pen for the ewe.

The retired lady sits on the seat of the lavatory in her splendid new wet-room with the lamb on her knee. She dries it and lays it in a nest of hay in a cardboard box by the heated towel rail. It is female. The retired lady is thinking that she will have to go out and try to milk the ewe. She had to do that once before, long ago, in another life. She remembers the trouble she had, the kicking over of the bucket and the pitiful amount of contaminated yellow liquid that she produced, flecked with mud and God knows what else. There is a knock at the door. It is Rhodri with a baby's feeding bottle and two sachets of colostrum.

Amazingly, once they have enlarged the hole in the teat, the lamb takes a feed, and another in the night. Next morning the lamb's front end is standing and her back-legs, albeit wobbly, are doing their best. Reluctant to get involved in long-term adoption, they return her to her mother – although at first they have to hold her up to reach the teat.

The mother has a far-away look in her eyes. She sniffs and nuzzles the lamb, absentmindedly. The lamb sniffs her back then wobbles along the mother's body, drawn to the smell of her milk or the warmth of the bare skin around the teat. She butts at the udder, which is what lambs do to let down the milk. She goes to latch on just as the ewe turns to see what is going on. The teat swings out of reach. The ewe nuzzles the lamb in vague recollection and the process begins again. The lamb is persistent and eventually successful, but the retired lady is not at all happy about the mental state of the ewe.

'She's got a lot of risk factors for failure to bond: first pregnancy, traumatic delivery, perinatal separation …'

'Don't be ridiculous! It's a sheep!'

They visit the vet and return with antibiotics and calcium injections, which are administered with unnatural ease.

'That ewe's not right.'

She stands looking into the distance, not grazing, not interested in ewe nuts and not drinking. The retired lady gives her water from a drench gun. The lamb stands by with its head hanging.

'I don't like to say anything, but that lamb isn't looking very chipper', says the retired gentleman. They take its temperature: it is far too low. The lamb is carried again into the wet-room. It turns its head from the cold bottle. They warm it and wrap the top of the bottle in wool from the mother but it doesn't seem to help. Then, as the retired lady sits on a stool, right up against the heated towel rail, looking forlornly at the lamb, it suddenly butts the side of her knee. She insinuates the teat of the bottle, so that it peeps out of the crook of her knee and the lamb fixes on the teat, emptying the bottle in seconds.

'It's my waterproof trousers!' calls the retired but triumphant lady. 'They smell right! They're the ones I had on when she was born; they got soaked in liquor.' The lamb does not look back, although the mother dies in the night despite their best endeavours.

'Whatever happened to beginner's luck?' They have nine more ewes to lamb and confidence is at an all-time low. Their beautifully tiled and finished wet-room – the only indication to their doubting friends that they might eventually knock this old building into some sort of presentable modern dwelling – has, in one fell swoop, been reabsorbed into the farm. It is, of course, perfectly adapted for the care of young animals – easy to clean, central plug-hole, indirect heat and running water. It has straw on its floor again, and the window that replaced the old pig-door can be opened onto the yard so that, in the weeks to come, Aby, the cade lamb, can explore the wider world in her own time. The retired gentleman looks into the wet-room where his wife, sitting on the lid of the loo, is giving the lamb its last ferocious feed of the day. 'Sometimes', he says, 'I think that this old place is reasserting itself.'

IO

Aby and the Earthquake

'I'D get that out of the house as soon as you can!' says Iolo, as he sits in the kitchen, looking down at the vigorous lamb that is butting his leg.

'Yes ... She only really comes in at night', replies the retired lady defensively (it is mid-morning).

'Maa!' says Aby the lamb, impatiently. The retired lady does not say proudly, *that's me!* She gets on with mixing up the next feed and then, with the bottle filled to the brim, she makes a point of leading the lamb outside and sitting on the doorstep to feed it while Iolo continues to drink his tea and to chew the cud with the retired gentleman.

The retired couple have noticed since they have lived in Mid-Wales that their Welsh neighbours are often reticent about giving direct advice. They have found it frustrating on occasions when they know that Dai the carpenter or Iestyn the mason know exactly how a job should be done but are reluctant to part with the information. Like good parents, it seems, they want the retired couple to work it out for themselves. It's the only way they will learn. As Iolo leaves he says, 'You get that lamb into the field with the other sheep as soon as you can.' The retired gentleman looks over his glasses at his wife. The significance of this direct injunction escapes neither of them.

'I know! I know … But the ewes all butt her away … quite viciously, and you can't expect her to sleep out there on her own … The fox will take her.'

Two weeks after Aby the sheep was born and the subsequent demise of her mother, leaving her an orphan, the other nine ewes start producing lambs. By this time Aby has settled to life in the house, where she sleeps in a large, plastic dog basket where the dog will occasionally join her (it is, after all, his basket). She must smell outrageous to a real sheep, and the prospects for ovine adoption are hopeless. Aby does not care. It is a tribute to the adaptability of such a small, traumatised creature that she is quite content to consider herself a dog, or a human for that matter, for the purposes of survival.

The one thing she does know is that she is not a sheep. So, as the retired lady and the dog see to the needs of the lambing flock, they are accompanied by Aby, who marches along next to Maa, being careful always to keep Maa between herself and the other ewes. They had initially looked at her quizzically, as if to say, 'Is that one of ours?' One sniff was enough for them to butt her away in disgust.

The rest of the lambing goes like magic. They check the ewes at dusk and dawn and often in the night, which is anyway short. A ewe will separate herself from the others, not by much. The next moment that they look, there is a lamb, up on its feet, baaing and suckling. The mother is making her gurgly, new-mother call and the retired couple run out and gather up the new-born lamb. They pronounce another ram lamb and spray its umbilicus with the magic purple spray, stencil its number on its side with orange spray and then carry it, bleating, leading the mother, into the fresh pasture in the next field. Eventually there are eight ram lambs including one set of twins and two more ewe lambs (no trouble).

The grass is slow to grow. Most of the fields face north, which is probably why they were not snapped up by local farmers. The retired lady feeds the ewes for a few more weeks. They look as if they need it. Lambing has left them thin and dishevelled, reminding the shepherd of her own experiences of parturition – going through the mill and emerging a different person. She walks through the collection of harassed and untidy ewes as the gang of rowdy ram lambs tear about down by the stream. A ewe calls to her lamb; a ram lamb replies without turning from the group. The ewe calls again; the lamb, still playing, answers again. Eventually and reluctantly the ram lamb breaks away from his peers and returns to his mother for a feed.

Immediately after birth the lambs stay close to their mothers, but with each successive day they gambol further, calling home from time to time for security. Aby does the same as she explores the yard.

'Maa!'

'Allo!' comes the reply from the kitchen.

All of a sudden, there is a tremendous baaing kerfuffle from the fields above the house. The retired lady goes running. The fields all interconnect. One of the ram lambs has strayed into an adjoining field. It can see its mother through the fence but cannot get to her. It baas in panic. All the mothers, hearing the lost lamb alarm, look up from grazing to check their own lambs. They call. The ram lambs call back ... 'Coming!' and carry on playing. For a moment there is general panic: ewes yelling, lambs running to the wrong ewes (they can't tell the difference until they are within sniffing range) – and still the plaintive cry of the one genuinely lost lamb fuelling the general panic. The retired lady puffs up the hill, through the gate which is kept open, and corners the lost little chap, picking him up and dropping him unceremoniously over the fence, forgetting for a moment that he is not a cat or a dog and is not fitted with a self-righting mechanism. He lands heavily, fortunately the right way up but with his legs splayed out in all directions, and bumps his chin on the ground.

'Whoops!' says the retired lady, 'Sorry!' He picks himself up and runs to his mother. At last, when all the lambs are standing by the correct mothers, the baaing ceases and everyone goes back to grazing and playing. The first few times this happens the retired lady feels quite carried away by the sense of emergency, but this hysterical lamb stock-taking or general 'stand by your Dam' takes place sufficiently frequently for the sense of urgency eventually to wear off.

Sometimes a ram lamb will wriggle under the fence into the woodland and will be unable to get back, so that its pathetic cries are punctuated by mouthfuls of precious sapling leaves.

Sometimes one gets its head stuck in the fencing. It is not long before the retired lady senses that the ewes are definitely changing their attitude to her. It seems to her that during a lost-lamb alert they not only baa for their own lambs, but come to the back of the house and baa at the kitchen window! Is it possible that they've actually worked out that it is somehow her responsibility to sort out their muddles?

The ewe lambs also play, but generally stay closer to their mothers. This is not surprising, as long before they are weaned the rumbustical, un-castrated ram lambs are sexually precocious – constantly practicing for their life-work with any woolly thing that does not butt them immediately. When Aby is left in the field with the other sheep (Maa watching from the house), Aby stays by the gate. The other lambs come and sniff her. They give her a little butt. She runs a little and they all follow. For a moment the retired lady thinks, with a little flush of pride, like a mother watching from the corner of the playground, 'Look! She's joining in.' A ram lamb puts its front feet on Aby's back and as she turns to free herself, another tries to mount her. She runs back to the gate.

'Maa!' Five of them are sniffing at her. 'Maa!' The ewes look up from grazing, their own ewe lambs safely by their sides, as if to say, 'It's just that little trollop from the house … Boys will be boys.' The retired lady can take no more: she whisks Aby out of the field to the safety of the yard where the lamb immediately seeks out the dog, and paws at his toy. The retired lady picks up the chewed, blue plastic boomerang and throws it. The dog runs to retrieve it, and Aby runs too, gambolling next to her friend who drops the boomerang at the lady's feet. They both look at her expectantly. She throws it again. Species dysphoria, thinks the retired lady: unhappy with your allocated species.

'Hopeless', sighs the retired gentleman, watching from the bathroom window.

The earthquake happens soon after – entirely metaphorical and without structural damage, but nevertheless everything shifts uneasily. The retired gentleman had been complaining of indigestion. His wife has cut down on the onions in his food. He has a few tests. One morning, following a bad bout of indigestion, he has a funny turn and his pulse is strangely rapid and irregular. Reality hits the retired lady like a train.

An hour later she is driving her car along the outside of the traffic in Newtown, following the ambulance, blue light flashing. The traffic lights turn red. She switches on her hazard warning lights, looks to left and to right and carries on. She is not about to lose him.

She is standing at the back door of the ambulance as it opens outside the Medical Admissions Unit at the Royal Shrewsbury Hospital, continuing the conversation that the closure of same had interrupted 60 miles earlier.

There then ensues a number of interviews with pale blue people and young ladies not in uniform who, when questioned, have to slip away and telephone. It soon becomes apparent that this is changeover day, the day when new house-officers get lost in the basement while looking for the path lab and walk confidently into broom cupboards.

'Are head injuries surgical or orthopaedic?'

'Do we routinely anticoagulate?'

Pale blue, home-grown people with no knowledge of other hospitals look on amazed, stunned by the general ignorance.

'What's that noise?' asks the house-officer.

'It's your crash bleep …' says a pale blue person.

'Cripes! I've got to go …' Houseman runs off. Houseman returns immediately and flustered to ask the way to Coronary Care. The retired lady feels quite nostalgic, but only for a moment.

Soon the retired gentleman is transferred to Coronary Care (presumably the houseman was too late and a bed has become unexpectedly vacant). People here are darker blue – reassuringly royal blue, and all is efficient and quiet, except for the incessant bleeping. The retired couple's grown-up children appear, joking nervously. The retired gentleman is fitted with stents and new pyjamas and is soon sitting up in bed, also joking nervously. The following day they are returning home. Already, as they wait in line to negotiate the traffic lights in Newtown, it all seems to have been a dream.

Green Sheep and the Rout of the English Knights

IT's hard enough to shear a large struggling ewe on a hot day with the midges biting and with general anxiety fuelling the sheep's already gassy disposition. But to do this with an audience and under constant threat of needlestick injury is no joke. So it is that Alfie, obliging son of Iolo (neighbour and ovine mentor to the retired couple), finds himself nominated by his equally obliging but considerably more wily father, to help them shear their moulting and motley crew of world-weary sheep.

'It's so difficult to catch them. If you don't mind, while you've got hold of them, I'll just jab 'em – watch out!' The retired lady lunges at the neck of the compromised ewe. Alfie's eyes widen and he shifts his own precarious neck from the needle's trajectory.

'There!' says the retired lady, stabbing the used syringe

into the top of a convenient fence post and picking up a much larger one, full of sticky white fluid and sporting a six-inch length of plastic tube instead of a needle. The ewe's head is now on the ground as Alfie frees the last of her fleece from just above her tail.

'I'll just squeeze in here and give her the jollop.' The retired lady's bulk is insinuated between the shearer and the gate, pushing him a little from his natural point of balance. She pushes the plunger to squirt the foul fluid into the ewe's throat, making her splutter and kick. At that exact moment the fleece is freed and the sheep is released from the shearer's grasp with a great kick and a shake and a cough. Alfie regains his balance, though not his composure. The retired lady is delighted.

'Didn't we do well?'

So the routine continues under the amused gaze of Alfie's friends and family. Iolo trims the feet of those that need it and fits the ridiculously large ear tags that the lady has ordered for the lambs – ones that she can see without her reading glasses; ones designed for bullocks. They shake their heads, wobbling their great dangly earrings like fortune tellers at a horse-fair. Miraculously, no-one except the sheep is injected or wormed, and in double-quick time the little flock is sheared and tidy and gleaming white, and everyone agrees, when pressed by the retired lady, that they are in remarkably good condition – all things considered.

All down the valley now, the ewes, freed from their bales of woolly insulation, are flexing their new found muscles and pulling in their deflated flanks. Lambs are thriving on the new grass, and the un-castrated ram lambs butt your proffered fist with enough force to melt the heart of a proud shepherd.

Farmers are caught up in this vanity, just as one views one's own children with secret wonderment. Between shearing and cutting the next batch of silage, the farmer's fantasy turns to agricultural accolade – it is show time! This is the time when the modest Welsh hill-farmer takes the best of his endeavours to show. He will measure himself and his animals against his peers and confirm his suspicions that he has produced a really tidy beast.

This happens from the smallest village show to the Royal Welsh. The whole family goes and bloodstock is assessed. As sons and daughters, home from agricultural college, lead their father's heifers and bulls around the showground, it is not necessarily the withers of the competing stock that catch their eyes! As a father lifts a tail and checks an udder, his daughter has to make her assessment in more subtle ways. Make no mistake, both have an eye for pedigree and vigour. Patriarchs, however, view potential sons-in-law with a good deal less enthusiasm than they do a new ram.

One daughter has overstepped the mark this year. Like the old Duchess of Windsor at her first party, who sported a scarlet sash in order to be noticed, this young farmer has, as many do, used the permitted ploy of dying her sheep with pale golden-blond sheep dye in order to attract the judges' and anyone else's attention.

'Green sheep! Amazing!' says the retired gentleman. 'Are these a new breed?'

'No. Bluefaced Leicester', says the girl, 'I didn't read the instructions properly!'

The retired couple have no in-laws to find at the local show this year. Sadly, all their children are busy elsewhere and all have a very independent attitude in these matters: a shame, thinks the retired lady as she watches the tug-of-war.

The retired gentleman is drinking draught bitter and talking diggers with a neighbour. In the showground, people dressed in historical costumes are forming up around the hay-bale ramparts for a re-enactment. The retired gentleman thinks it would be much more fun for everyone if they had more weapons and live ammunition.

The chairman of the show committee has had the same thought. There are a couple of musket shots and a salvo of arrows (boring – no one is hurt). Then a couple of medieval knights have a punch-up and the crowd are invited to decide the fate of the loser: he dies a horrible death and is carried away dripping blood (better). The other knights, with their pikes and halberds and their armour that squeaks, are heading towards the beer tent when a challenge is issued over the Tannoy.

From every corner of the field, as in Hamlyn, children flow out, from the produce tent and the tea tent, from behind their mother's skirts, climbing over animal pens and from behind hedges. All mass on the edge of the showground where our chairman is issuing arms: four-foot lengths of pipe insulation, one to every child from the tiniest toddler to the gangliest teenager. They test them, flailing the air. The knights creak as they shuffle from foot to foot, nervously, where the announcement has stopped them in their tracks. A siren sounds.

There is a deafening roar. Teachers all around the ground feel faint with panic as 100 armed and fearless young Welshmen and women (some very young indeed) with blood-curdling screams of glee, set about the rout of the historical re-enactment society.

Men in armour flee in all directions pursued by swarms of

whooping, blue-bladed warriors. They are dragged screaming from haystacks and from under the skirts of their tents as they try to find sanctuary. The Black Knight, for once fearful for his life, wealds his wooden broadsword to parry the worst of the insulation-lashing dealt by six little girls in summer frocks who have chased him up the hay-bale rampart and are about to knock him off the top. The crowd roars its approval. The St John's ambulance prepares for casualties as dead knights, mostly elderly and overweight, lie panting all around the field, small boys still hitting them (that's much better).

Then there is the spectacle of local axemen accomplishing the most amazing feats of strength, agility and self-confidence as they narrowly avoid amputation. They race to cut up tree trunks in the most unlikely and ill-advised ways, standing on branches and up poles.

Dog-racing next. 'This should be worth seeing,' says the retired gentleman, anticipating canine mayhem. Their own dog Pedro is not going to compete. 'He'll be alright', say the neighbours. The retired gentleman explains that it's just a question of vet's bills. Only last month Pedro managed to unzip himself jumping over a barbed wire fence, and it cost £70. Then there was £55 for the bitten paw. If he gets overexcited and picks a fight, we could end up paying out for all the other dogs as well.

Pedro, meanwhile, is sitting to attention, sporting a large scarlet rosette: it is not for Best in Show but for the dog the judge would most like to take home. Someone is taking his photograph.

The first heat, for small terriers, is already lining up, the dogs straining at their leashes before the organisers have

finished rigging up the hare. The hare is in fact a dead rabbit attached to a string run around a number of large pulleys
(car wheel contraptions) and finally attached to a dismem-
bered bicycle which is pedalled by a man lying on his back. It
hauls the hare around the U-shaped course at extraordinary
speed before it disappears down a pipe. The starter is waving the 'hare' at the first line of contenders who are yapping
and straining. The hooter sounds: the dogs are loosed, heads
down, bodies elongated, feet hardly touching the ground.
Owners who have released dogs now stampede to the finish
to shout and scream and wave toys and favourite bones. As
the 'hare' pops down the hole into the pipe and the dogs cross
the finishing line, they all peel off to their individual owners to be petted and congratulated. There are several heats of
terriers, then the medium-sized dogs – spaniels and the like.
Sheepdogs follow, then hounds – not pack-hounds but retired
greyhounds and a whippet.

Considering the excitement of the crowd and the enthusiasm of the dogs, the event is extraordinarily orderly. These
dogs are all peerless professionals. 'It does seem very well
organised', admits the retired gentleman with a tinge of dis-
appointment. For show purposes, Pedro Gonzales would
seem to be nearest to a Labrador (albeit Spanish); more of a
large retriever than a hound. This is the last heat before the
finals and the retired gentleman relents due to peer pressure.

Pedro lines up with Labradors, golden retrievers and a
bulldog (please God, don't let him pick on the bulldog). The
hooter hoots: they're off! Definitely not so competitive. They
are the canine equivalent of the beer-tent crowd. Pedro trots
along with them, sniffing their bottoms and generally getting
in the way, oblivious of the hare; and then he spots Dai in the

crowd and peels off to say hallo. Dai waves his arms around and shouts encouragement. Pedro is puzzled and looks away. Something catches his eye on the home straight. He remembers the others, who are now well into their stride. He puts on a little spurt, crossing the field from near the start to near the finish, leaving out most of the course (very intelligent) and ploughs into the leading group, knocking a couple over – but they don't want to play. He hears the retired lady screaming and lollops over to her, tail wagging, unplaced and disqualified. The retired gentleman is swelled with pride – what a sportsman! It's the taking part that counts – and no vet's bill!

Meanwhile, the fiercely competitive terriers and sheepdogs are preparing for the finale, which is a Derby open to all classes. Baying fills the air. The retired couple decide to quit while ahead. They reattach Pedro's rosette and take him to join the spectators. The race is run to a mighty roar that fills the valley. Every dog on the field (bar one) busts its guts for fame and glory; it runs the course and then throws itself upon the now bedraggled 'hare'. There is a whirlpool of frenzied dog around the hole down which the hare has gone. Owners grab tails and pull. Doggy tempers are frayed; snaps are exchanged. It is all, as they say, about to kick off. The steward of the course wades in with his special steward's boot which he insinuates into the maelstrom, then gently but very rapidly lifts, splashing a wave of Jack Russells in every direction, buffeting the flotsam of rolling sheepdogs, to be grabbed by owners, all in amazingly jovial spirits. The retired couple view this expression of jolly, doggy fun with wonder. They remember the village hall committee in the Midlands that banned the annual dog show because of overwhelming health and safety issues.

As the spectators stroll, laughing, back to the marquees, little dogs are held up and tousled in triumph; big ones on hind legs lick tears of mirth from proud owner faces, and the remaining un-captured curs – the real heroes of the day – continue their chase across the fields that rise up beyond the showground. The lead animal (possibly a sheepdog) seems to have a small terrier attached to its bottom, holding on by its teeth.

This pack is pursued by a little flotilla of gesticulating human figures whose body language at this distance appears perhaps a little less than jolly.

12

Safe in the Gleam of Tony Blair's Smile

IT is August and there are birthdays to celebrate. The retired couple who have settled in the Trannon valley, renovating the old farmhouse and tending its fields and woodland, are having a weekend off to mark the birthdays of their first-born.

The cade lamb has finally been evicted from the wet-room – which has been power-washed and gleams like Tony Blair's smile.

It is a gloriously sunny day, but the grown-up children of the family are now happy to disport themselves in the new-found comfort of the old farmhouse. Their stomachs are moaning softly with gastronomic overload; they are mellow and content to sit in the cool, laptops nestling with them on the sofas, as they show each other their different virtual worlds.

The retired gentleman, having umpired the cricket and cooked the barbecue, did not eat his lunch and has now gone to bed. The retired lady looks worried.

'He's not right', she tells his elder son, 32 today. 'He won't admit it. Ever since he had that do in June he won't tell me if he's feeling ill. He thinks I'll shunt him off to hospital again.' Number-one-son goes up to talk to his dad. He comes down again almost immediately.

'He's got a pain in his chest. He's used his puffer and it hasn't helped. In fact, it's got worse. He knows you will want to call an ambulance and he knows you are right … So I think you better had.'

The retired lady feels the panic rising in her neck as she looks in the address book for the sheet of paper with all the emergency numbers and their map reference. Her elder daughter, 30 yesterday, slips quietly past her and goes up to sit with her stepdad.

'Where are the bloody numbers!' the retired lady rushes upstairs and rummages frantically in the pile of papers under the bag of medicines on the bedside table. 'Never mind. I'll look up Shrop-Doc in the Phone book. Where are my glasses?' She glances at her husband who looks strange, not ill – sun-tanned and sort of stubborn, like a wilful child. She runs downstairs and starts flipping frantically through the phone book.

'What will it be under? Powys council? I don't know.' It feels like a nightmare.

'Mum! The numbers are in the piano stool!' comes a shout from upstairs. Sure enough, there they are. She dials the emergency doctor. After an interminable time she is put through to a human being, then to a doctor. She tells her story and is told to call 999.

'Well! I could have done that in the first place … Whatever

happened to arranged admissions direct to CCU!' she grumbles as she dials again. She repeats the story. An ambulance is on its way. She goes back up and sits on the bed. She feels her husband's pulse and looks at him. He looks himself.

He says he thinks it might be easing off a bit and that he is sorry that he hid the numbers.

The ambulance is directed to the door by stewards recruited from the family, who are only just there in time, so quickly does it come. This time there is no dicing with death, chasing the blue light through Newtown; there is no jumping of red lights. The retired lady is loaded into the ambulance with her husband. He breaths his oxygen quietly as they rattle along in the old vehicle.

The paramedic recounts his own life-story. It is very calming and very reassuring to be in the hands of a man who knows what is important in life. The life of the retired couple is in the hands of a man who has put his own life in order; he has renounced the rat-race and found peace and stability in rural Mid-Wales; he is a man who keeps chickens. When he pauses to do observations the retired lady's thoughts turn to myocardial matters, to blocked stents and abnormal rhythms. Her mind is spinning. She concentrates on reading all the signs in Welsh and practices changing the verbs to suit any occasion. By the time they reach Shrewsbury she can fluently discuss oxygen cocks, not banging your head and the legal consequences of abusing ambulance personnel in both languages.

Despite these unpromising beginnings this admission goes surprisingly well. True, there are reports in the local press that the good-looking junior doctor (instantly recognised by the eldest daughter – funny that) has only recently been released from detention under the Prevention of Terrorism Act. However, he is released without charge and everyone agrees what an exceptionally gifted young doctor he is. In fact they all are. The retired gentleman's Tesco's leisure suit, which he had omitted to hide, still fits and his stents are still both working. He has had only a small myocardial infarction and will be home soon.

The next day (where did that night go?) the family celebrate with organic sirloin steak and goat's cheese from the farm shop on the way home, having collected the retired lady from the hospital.

At home they are greeted, as usual, by their very good neighbours waiting for news of the invalid and with news of their own. 'Tilla, the retired couple's hen, who has been sitting, has, this very afternoon, hatched 11 bantam chicks from eggs donated by another retired couple in Lludiart-y-Waun. The twelfth egg, which had not hatched, has been tested by floating in warm water (Jeremy and his wife know about birds). The egg in question did not bob in time to a little beating heart within, so has been discreetly removed so as not to distract the hen or distress the family. The little fluffy yellow and orange balls scurry around the yard, already pecking at invisible mites on the ground. They move about as if demonstrating entropy, bouncing off each other in seemingly random movement – yellow billiard balls in perpetual motion.

'Tilla clucks and spreads her wings and 11 little balls rush under her umbrella. That's odd; it's not raining. A shadow crosses the yard – they look up: a buzzard circles five metres above.

'Quick, where's the bucket?'

Everyone forms a circle around the chicks. The dog joins in. One by one the chicks are caught and popped into the bucket. One runs towards Pedro: snap! – the dog stands tight-lipped and wide-eyed. The chick is gone.

'Drop it Pedro!' yells everyone. The dog opens his mouth and the chick jumps out, unscathed, straight into the bucket!

When all the chicks are safely gathered in and the hen grabbed, all are rushed (*nee-nor*) to the designated place of safety – the pristine wet-room! The last bottle required for essential human grooming is removed. 'Tilla pecks at something pink and coiled in the corner.

'Hey 'Tilla! Get off my thong!' A daughter retrieves her underwear and Jeremy's wife unloads the chicks, sexing them as she goes:

'Male … Male … Male … Male … Have I got this right? Male. This chick is wet!'

'That'll be Jonah!' says one of the heads poking round the door. Jeremy's wife looks round and, with relief in her voice, refutes the suggestion.

'No, it's definitely Joan!'

The eldest son and his girlfriend are able to stay until the retired gentleman returns home. He has now stopped smoking again and his uncharacteristic testiness is enhanced by his new medication which, it announces in its blurb, may give migrainous headaches for up to two weeks. It does.

The last of the family depart. For the first time in their lives, it seems, the tables might be turning. What are we going to do about x? (where 'x' is the child causing the most anxiety at that moment) changes, for a moment, in this one episode, into: what are we going to do about Dad?

'Payback-time!' says the retired gentleman, rubbing his hands together.

'Not quite yet, I don't think', says the retired lady, 'but there are very promising signs. They really all were a great help and so supportive.'

The gentleman retires to bed with a Sudoku and two paracetamol. His wife explores the mysteries of Black and Decker as she constructs her first brooder.

This is a timber and chicken-wire tent that will ward off aerial attack and protect the seven delinquent baby cockerels and four little hens who are currently testing the ammonia resistance of the shower-room grout.

'Another learning curve', thinks the retired lady as she eventually figures out how to stop the electric screwdriver going backwards. Soon she understands why foxes and badgers gain access to chicken runs with such alacrity. These days the mesh is manufactured in such a way that it unzips when put under uneven pressure, laddering like a pair of tights then falling into pieces (she feels a letter to the newspaper coming on but dismisses the impulse).

She resolves to return the remainder of her faulty roll to the shop. Meanwhile, she sits on the ground beneath the bedroom window in the evening sunshine, and darns her brooder with galvanised wire. Above her, the retired gentleman is looking down, slowly shaking his head.

13

Pumpkins, Myths and Toadstools

IT is October. Mists cling in the cleavage of the hills and dusk surprises them every afternoon. Although the retired couple have only been to Llanidloes for an early evening drink, it is dark as they drive home over the moor. They stop on the high ground to retrieve their voicemail, pulling into a gateway and turning off the lights, extinguishing the myriad sheep eyes turned inquisitively upon them. As the retired gentleman busies himself with the mobile phone, the lady gets out and walks around the vehicle. It is windy up here and the night is raven black. She can smell sheep on the swirling, damp breeze and there is invisible movement all around, a sporadic cough, a sudden flap of wings. One of her hands touches the car as she stands there feeling the moorland with all her senses except her eyes, which she opens and closes. It makes no difference. Take away that hand and she would be lost ...

Curses from the driver's window recall her. She gets back

in. There is low cloud and the phone reception keeps coming and going, garbling the family's intentions for the following half-term week. They will arrive when they arrive.

The retired gentleman releases the handbrake and depresses the clutch. They roll out of the gateway and onto the gentle slope of the moorland road. He releases the clutch and with a little jolt the engine starts. He belongs to a generation that never takes starters or batteries for granted. A little further, their progress is interrupted by an accident which is completely blocking the narrow carriageway. It is not a policeman that signals for them to stop but a Tawny Owl, standing officiously in the middle of the road by the casualty, holding them up as it busily pulls strips of carrion from a wild thing squashed firmly onto the centre of the country lane. They watch for several minutes as the great bird stomps around this convenient road-kill, viewing it from different angles, its head on one side, then the other; it pulls off another strip. It looks into the dipped headlights of the car from time to time, but unable to make out anything useful returns to the kill. When it has satisfactorily freed the prey, it grasps it in its talons and flaps off into the night.

They continue down the hill, the banks now steep on either side. That is when they see it. In an instant it flashes across their path, leaping from one bank to the other. They both see it clearly – well enough to agree that it is male, large and long, extended as it bounds over them, the image from a brooch or a weather vane. What they are not so sure about is the colour. Both see it, then doubt themselves. Is it somehow in its own shadow or has their path just been crossed by a black fox? ... *The* black fox?

Next morning, the retired lady consults the internet:

mythical tales abound. What they saw is plainly the tormented soul of a local deceased and notorious hunter. She consults her elder daughter, the one with the degree in genetics. She seems to think that you can get melanism (whatever that might be) in any species. She casually asks her neighbours if they have ever heard of, or seen, such a beast: they have not! Is there a slight reticence in their answer? She wonders who amongst the local hunters died in strange circumstances; who turned in their grave when the hunt ban came in. She refrains from asking.

There are four small pumpkins sitting on the kitchen table, one for each grandchild (this is a loose term applied to people, two generations removed, to whom one is related by common law, divorce, happenstance or, occasionally, by blood). The retired lady is rummaging in the kitchen drawer for knives. They must be sharp enough to incise the skin of the squash without removing the digits of the four precious children in their care. Thus the four set about their delicate task with their excellent coordination, sharp eyesight and quick reflexes exercised to the limits by inadequate tools. They wrestle with blunt potato peelers and picnic knives. The faces of Halloween are, in consequence, more grotesque than ever. The retired couple are absent upstairs, applying a plaster to the lady's finger which is bleeding profusely. She has managed to stab herself with the only really sharp knife in the house.

Sadly, this Halloween night, there are not a lot of comings and goings in their lane; but when Jeremy and his wife come home from work, well after dark, eerie flickering lights watch them from the bushes. Jeremy's wife smiles to herself, with the confidence of a woman who knows she has sugared eyeballs to hand!

Meanwhile, in the old farmhouse, black bin bags are being mutilated as hysteria rises. Pedro the dog won't stop wagging his tail, which tears the bin bag that he is wearing so that he keeps tripping over it and tearing it some more. Grandad fixes him with gaffer tape. Faces are whitened with make-up (not scary enough); they are powdered with talc. The dog sneezes. The cat – scary enough without enhancement – has, nevertheless, been caught in the powdery crossfire. She plays safe and withdraws to the top of the Welsh dresser, a shadow of her former self. The pots wobble ominously.

A witch's hat has been made (the only card they have is white but she can be a white witch). Vampire teeth are being cut from cardboard (not easy with a bandaged finger). The retired lady's Yves Saint Lauren lipstick, the one she got last Christmas, is liberally applied to puncture holes in necks. The elder granddaughter's recently acquired sophistication has now lapsed completely as they rush around the house in a cloud of sweet-smelling dust in search of a mirror. Grandad remembers that there is one in the wardrobe waiting to be screwed to the door. He holds it up, and for a moment all is quiet as they stand transfixed by their own dreadful image. Ghoulish or what?

The lanterns are retrieved for a photo-call and ghostly creaks and wails are tried. Pedro needs howling practice. Unlike the couple's previous dog – a German Shepherd – Pedro has never really got the hang of howling. Everyone shows him. He looks puzzled, furrowing his powdered brow, and wags his tail, rustling his bin bag.

The retired couple hold back as the five awful spectres wobble along the uneven, moon-lit track towards their neighbours' house. Well, four wobble and hang on to each other in the dark; the fifth knows exactly where he is going.

They clutch their lighted lanterns. One goes out and has to be relit by Grandad who materialises mysteriously from the bushes.

'Wait for us, Pedro.'

The great yew tree casts a long, gothic shadow at the cross-roads, and here the grandparents shelter unseen as the children venture to the neighbours' front door in their scariest excursion yet. An owl hoots. One reaches up to clang the rusty bell. Nothing happens. They shuffle uncomfortably, rattling their chains. The boldest boy (but not very bold) knocks the door with his scythe. The cork falls off the tip. Nothing happens (neighbours know about suspense). The children look into the darkness behind them for guidance. Silence is their only reply. The door flies open and they are bathed in yellow light. They are turned to stone, petrified by their own bloodcurdling appearance and the spookiness of this unfamiliar reality …

That is all that is required. Spooks are, after all, essentially passive. The neighbours are initially terrified, they scream and scatter. Then curiosity and morbid interest overcome them.

They get out the sugared eyeballs, worms and ghoulish brew, and the ghost of a notorious black Labrador eats their dog's supper.

The following day is misty and the moonlit crispness of the previous night has produced a ground frost, the first of the autumn. The bracken, which has stood up well this year, has now darkened to the colour of bull's blood and is now falling. This is a woodland emergency and the retired lady calls all hands to the rescue. The bracken control measures this year have been less than adequate due, in part, to Grandad being poorly in the late spring. Falling bracken knocks over saplings.

The grandchildren are midge-proofed and anoraked and piled into Grandad's dumper truck for transportation to the front line where they swarm over the hillside, as only children can, releasing bending oak treelets from the frantic grasps of dying bracken.

'I've saved another tree!' sounds the joyful mantra as they rush from tree to tree. The retired lady would never have guessed that such a tedious and back-breaking job could be such fun. And, as the trees pop up above the maroon quilt of matted bracken the children find other treasures. There are crowds of tiny toadstools and a giant puffball the size of a cabbage, huge parasol mushrooms with curly tops, and fly agarics – the red ones with white spots that the creepy-crawlies love to eat. Do they hallucinate? All of the finds are photographed – the orange and pink fungi that split and contort into amazing shapes, the staghorns and the bracket fungus on the dead tree. At the end of the day the retired lady, seeing the woodland through child's eyes, is exhausted by the wonder and the newness of it all. After tea, photographs are emailed to parents and, 'good as gold', two little boys lie on their mattress, still and quiet for a few moments, until the retired lady is fast asleep on the sofa and they can resume their animated discussions of the day.

14

The Folly of the Four-by-Four

I T is the end of the farming year. The Single Farm Payment form has been filled in and sent and the acknowledgement letter filed. The harvest is gathered in. The barns are full and battle lines of giant, shiny black silage bags are formed around the curtilages of the local farms – ramparts against the winter. They are three deep at the base, two deep on the second tier with a row of single bales along the top. In places they curve around the contours of the hills, clearly visible from right across the valley. They are a public statement of prudent husbandry and rising feed prices. Indoors, the farmer's wife stands on a chair to add the last of her damson chutney to the ranks of jars on the uppermost shelf of the pantry. If only governments were as provident.

Even the retired couple have managed to make some hay, which is piled in a haphazard stack on pallets in the sheep shed. Iolo cut it for them, but it is so long since hay was taken from the meadow that the ground, worked for many years only by moles, is very uneven. There is as much earth and root in the hay as there is grass. The field is left with bald patches, and when it comes to baling Iolo's small baler will not go up the steep incline into the field. It is also the busiest time of the farming year, when all the neighbours are working from dawn to dusk and well into the night getting in their own winter feed. Gwyn, another neighbour who keeps a watchful eye over the hedge, takes pity on them and turns it once for them with his tedder (a giant rotary rake). The retired lady then buys a pitchfork, and she and her daughter turn it again by hand and load it onto their old open-top trailer, and the retired gentleman tows it to the barns with the now decrepit camper-van.

Tomorrow is harvest festival, when several new pick-ups will disport themselves outside the chapel. Lamb prices are at an all-time record high and, with the papers full of dire predictions about the economy, truck-dealers have been slashing their prices to unload their stock before Armageddon.

The retired gentleman is in the yard, sitting in the five-seater cab of the couple's new Ford Ranger, practicing putting it in and out of four-wheel drive, and working out what all the warning lights mean. The wheel arches are already caked with mud after their first excursion up to the top field to show the sheep. Even in two-wheel drive, the off-road tyres give amazing grip.

During their years in England the couple had ranted about the folly of the 4x4. 'Chelsea tractors' were doing the school run. Elegant ladies in snakeskin shoes complained about the lack of parking, yet were unwilling or unable to park their monstrous Mercedes off-road tanks on the grass.

Having brought up all their children to challenge everything that they hear, the couple have been getting some of their own medicine. The children, all grown-up, have been asking with glee about diesel consumption, emissions, impending increases in road tax, peer pressure, inability to resist a bargain, pressure sales, insurance premiums and whether the retired lady will be able to park, reverse, get in and out of – and possibly, when she does eventually clamber in, see out of – the new vehicle! The retired gentleman counters with the unique condition of the market, high altitude, unpredictable weather cycles, poor health increasing the dangers of isolated living, etc.

Now, the retired couple (unlike some farmers) did not buy their brand new 4x4 in order to absorb their huge operating profit and avoid the incumbent crippling tax. This year, after the sale of their crop of fat lambs – the seven ram lambs from their first lambing – they did make a profit, a modest profit, a very modest profit. 'Double figures – if you don't count the new vehicle', the retired lady hears herself justifying plaintively to the accountant. He is shaking his head. 'We are just building up our flock, you see.' He looks hopeful and asks, by how many animals the flock has increased this year. There is hesitation.

'Three ... But we lost two ewes.'

'So, that's a net gain of one, is it?' The retired lady gives a forlorn nod.

The accountant does not ask how long, at this rate, it will take the flock to build up, but he does explain that they will have to make a profit at least now and again (say every five years or so) or the revenue won't accept that they are a proper business. Under those circumstances the partnership will have to pay back any tax that they have saved in previous years. He asks about the possibility of diversification, bed and breakfast, fishing weekends, producing something with their own wool.

'I think we get the message', says the retired gentleman.

On the way home they stop at a farm they know. They buy ten ewe lambs – hoggs, which are sheep that have not yet reached their first shearing. In their new profit-led mind-set they moan about the price. Gareth the farmer assures them, with his customary good humour, of the outstanding quality of these end-of-season hoggs, and quotes the astronomical prices reached for inferior beasts in the livestock market at Dolgellau only last week. They look doubtful. He throws in six weeks free use of one of his young tups, for their other ewes. He will bring them all down tomorrow. They shake hands.

Next day the retired lady goes and calls Aby, the cade lamb, who brings all the other sheep down to the pen by the gate where the lady has left a bucket of feed. For once, when she pulls the concealed rope, the gate of the pen closes smoothly and fastens with a click. None of the sheep escape. Once they have finished the concentrate, she calls the retired gentleman and they filter out the eight ewes that are to go to the bargain-offer ram. When these are safely chased away and shut in another field the retired lady sets about transporting the remaining three pubescent ewe lambs that were bred on the farm, and for which she has a considerable affection, to a place of safety for the duration of the ram's visit. She refills the treat-bucket with a little more concentrate and sets off with Aby to the farthest field, on the other side of the woodland. Aby happily walks to heel and the other two follow.

Sheep are not particularly cuddly but they do like to be close to the ones they love, especially when a bucket of concentrate is involved. Aby presses against the lady's leg in a proprietorial fashion, tending to trip her as they walk up the track. The other two virgin sheep dawdle behind until the retired gentleman brings up the rear with a stick. Later that day Gareth arrives with the new hoggs. They are delicate-framed and lively, with large, dark, intelligent eyes and sharp ears (disposition of ears, expressed on an analogue clock face, five to one – that's the best time for ears according to Gareth; ten to two – sluggish and out of condition; quarter to three – usually sick; twenty to four – call the vet). Simple, thinks the retired lady, once she has finally worked out what he is talking about.

The hoggs are taken to the place of safety, above the wood with the three virgins, well away from the new tup, which Gareth drops off near the house in the field with the eight breeding ewes. They are manifestly pleased to see him (disposition of ears – definitely veering towards midday). The retired lady tries not to dwell on the fact that he has travelled down from Gareth's farm in the same trailer as her ten beautiful new, virgin ewes that are to grow and mature for optimal and profitable breeding next year.

As the retired lady goes to the house to get the holding number to write on Gareth's movement order she notices a dry chill in the air, and she fancies she sees a snowflake.

Six inches of snow have fallen over night and the retired lady is at the far side of the yard piling firewood onto a child's sledge. Pedro the dog is wearing a strange harness contraption and is jumping around in great excitement. He pushes his already snowy nose into a drift, snorts and splutters, sending a spray of powdery flakes into the air, onto which he pounces. Then he chases his tail.

The retired lady laughs and throws a piece of firewood into the middle of the yard. The dog hares after it, overshooting in a flurry of snowflakes, rolling several times and coming to a panting rest with his mouth open and his tongue hanging out. Large flakes are falling and, as they land on his panting tongue, he snaps at the air again and again, zigzagging and swerving to snap in all directions catching snowflakes before they hit the ground.

The retired gentleman, watching from the open bedroom window, shouts down that she'd be better using the wheelbarrow. She waves her gloved hand dismissively and yells back something that sounds like *testing prototype*. She now appears to be trying to attach the rope from the sledge to the harness on the dog. She removes one glove and drops it. The dog picks it up then chases his tail again. Shouting ensues. The voice is deepened and the dog responds (temporarily), sitting to attention by the sledge, albeit facing in the wrong direction and with a glove in his mouth. There is mumbling and half-gloved fumbling as the retired lady tries to explain to Pedro the principles of the dog-sled. He cocks his head onto one side and furrows his snowy brow into a most intelligent frown. Slowly she leads him forward, taking up the slack in the rope. The sledge begins to move. She resists the temptation to run back to it and jump on shouting *Mush!* – there are already several bottom-shaped indentations in the snow to remind her that her balance may not be quite as good as it was last time she played out on a snowy morning. Talking calmly to the dog they proceed across the yard veering towards the front door of the cottage. However, the sledge is quite low for the depth of snow and a considerable bow-wave is accumulating in front of this prototype dog-sled, which may, in the end, turn out to be a snow-plough. As the curve of the trajectory increases it digs itself in and turns over, spilling kindling and logs all about, and delighting the dog who now understands completely and runs in ever decreasing circles around the retired lady – until, tied together inexorably, they fall over in the snow.

15

The Big Freeze

THE snow will last from December to March, and even then the grass will not grow for another two months, so sharp are the frosts and dry is the spring. It is a very testing winter.

Initially the retired lady rises with enthusiasm at dawn, which thankfully is now at a more reasonable hour. She dons her boots and waterproof trousers (the hallmark of a real farmer) and sets off, every morning, trudging through the crunching snow, up their own cwm to feed the young sheep; the new ones tamer every day. Aby, the cade lamb, is now fully grown but will never be quite normal – always untidy and shouting in her disinhibited ovine way. From the first moment the retired lady's yellow coat appears over the horizon Aby is yelling 'Maa!' and galloping down the hillside, giving her call a distinct, coarse vibrato. This does a lot to break the ice with the other sheep who cannot help being fascinated by the spectacle. Soon, the two brightest of the hoggs that came from Gareth are dancing around Aby as the retired lady tries to open the stiff gate with Aby fervently pushing it from the other side. Aby walks importantly up the field in step with the retired lady to fill up a distant trough for the more nervous sheep, then back to the gate for her own food, more bonded to the mother-bucket than to any other receptacle. This allows the others to get their fair share. Pedro, who has been lying down outside the field, behaving himself and not upsetting the other sheep, can now be called and leaps over the gate into the field to sniff Aby critically. Not infrequently Aby dives headlong into the white plastic bucket before Maa has time to put it down. Then the handle hooks itself around her neck, so that when she pauses for breath and lifts her head the bucket comes too and she trots around with it over her head, a modern mythical beast emitting muffled baas. The retired lady unhooks the bucket, laughing, then unpicks bramble from the sheep's now huge and unruly fleece and Pedro licks her malty face – what a mess!

The following morning, as the sun peeks over the cleft in the hill and the golden rays illuminate the hoar frost on the great oak trees, beyond them, on the sunny upper slope beneath a clear blue sky, something catches the retired lady's eye. It is a creature, black against the gleaming alpine bank, moving like a big cat, low and sleek but with a long, thick, curved tail, concave upwards – a black panther? – with a bushy tail … Realisation dawns – a black fox, thinks the retired lady – The black fox! A shock of excitement grips her. She crouches on the track. Her glasses are on the kitchen table. The binoculars and camera are hanging under the coats on the back of the kitchen door. She holds her clenched fist to her left eye to make a pin hole through which to see more clearly. With her other hand, she steadies the dog. Their scent is held in the pool of cool valley air that surrounds them. Above, the black fox flops down in the morning sun. Moments later it moves away, diagonally across the hillside to the gap in the hedge, near to the spot where it had crossed their path on that dark night in the autumn. But, from its spot in the snow something else is moving, a small black dot runs directly up the hill to the cover of the hedge. It has a cub.

The ram has now returned to his own farm so, as the snow gets thicker and the ground more frozen, the couple bring the young sheep down to a field near the house. This makes twice daily feeding, filling up the hay-racks, breaking ice and carrying water a lot easier.

'How much do you think I should be feeding them? All the books say something different', the retired lady asks her reluctant mentor, Iolo, when next he calls.

'As much as they want.'

'Maa!' says Aby emphatically; 'told you so', from the other side of the fence. Iolo catches the lady's look of hopeless frustration and adds, 'You didn't have them scanned, did you … Those blocks of concentrate are good and then they can pretty well take what they need.'

Next day, the retired lady can be seen rolling a large, heavy wheel of concentrated goodness, enriched with fish oil (she's not at all sure about that) up the icy field in clouds of puffing steamy breath. She cuts a circle out of the plastic covering on one side so the sheep can lick and rasp at it with their teeth, and day by day it can slide down, migrating towards the house as it gets smaller and smaller. In a very short time the plastic cover, licked clean, is nosed under the gate by the back door – more please!

The retired gentleman slips his mysterious other gear stick into 'L4' as they drive up the cwm (they are going to risk the scenic route). Up the hill the snow is packed, but someone has gritted the steepest parts. The stream slides down the gorge by the road, almost silently, lubricated by the cold. The snow on either side has frozen and forms a sheet that overhangs the water, almost bridging the stream in places. The couple stop to take in the scene and a Spanish Labrador – more Spanish today – demonstrates quixotic disregard for danger as he trots across an ice bridge to rescue the object of his desire. The retired couple exchange a glance; they know they shouldn't do it. They throw the ball again and again to the other side of the stream as the skating dog explores this novel environment to their great amusement. Sometimes he crosses with a great bounding leap, or slides along the ice to a narrow part and hops over. His confidence is building.

'Come on – one more last time. We must get on', says the retired gentleman as he lobs the ball another final time across the gorge. They turn towards the tailgate in anticipation of the dog's imminent return, when there is a loud crack and a Spanish Labrador, suddenly a windmill of legs and spray, is tumbling into the water. The water isn't deep and Labradors are impervious to cold but there now ensues an object lesson in why falling into frozen ponds is not a good idea.

Slippery sides and no grip make extrication difficult – even with four-wheel drive and off-road tyres, which dogs undoubtedly possess. Complicated instructions and advice are shouted, gesticulations indicate preferred routes. The dog looks puzzled. A lady with less-than-perfect balance and inadequate gearing descends the bank. A gentleman wonders where his wife has put the winch and the tow-rope. A Spanish Labrador wags his tail. He knows he shouldn't do it. He doesn't leap out and bound up the bank. He stands in the water and gives a little shiver. Gravity acting on a middle-aged lady and curiosity acting on a dog results in a rendezvous at the lowest section of the brook, where the stream enters a large culvert under a side road. Here, both are eventually hauled to safety. The dog shakes itself with amazing efficacy. All are now equally wet. Honour is served.

They resume their adventure, up and onto the moor, through the high-walled white canyon made by the snow-plough. The sun is setting on the huge, rolling, snow-covered hills of Mid-Wales. The misty scene is suffused with a lilac glow. The waters of the Clywedog Reservoir are deep and black and unreflecting – hungry for light. In the distance the silhouettes of sheep can just be seen, drawing a line across the otherwise featureless hillside as they proceed in single file across the icy waste, from the silage cage by the road to the shelter of the hedge where they will spend a crystal-encrusted night. Driving to the agricultural supplier, they congratulate themselves on their timely and uncharacteristically extravagant purchase of a new four-wheel drive vehicle with off-road tyres. There is room for six sacks of ewe nuts, two of chicken feed, four more heavy cartwheels of fishy stuff, two vitamin buckets, four pints of milk, a loaf of bread for the lady in the dell, and a wet dog. The retired lady joins the queue of men in flat hats and waterproof trousers. She enjoys her wait by the space heater and wonders if she smells, as her eye is drawn to the clock where a promotional cardboard ram rocks, about his business, driven by the ticking of the mechanism. She looks away. At last, she proffers her debit card to the harassed warehouse man. Business has never been so brisk – not since the winter of '62–'63. The contents of the warehouse are ominously dwindling.

A couple of pints of beer in town and they can refresh their repertoire of tales of frozen water-pumps, blocked cesspits and young people who just don't know how to drive in the snow anymore. These they will carry back to their neighbour, with her bread, as she waits for her tea without the luxury of a new four-wheel drive vehicle with off-road tyres.

16

Raining, Cats and Dog

SPRING appears to have been cancelled this year, the retired lady is telling her stepdaughter on the telephone. From the relative tropical paradise of Cornwall, the listener is surprised to hear that the retired couple still have snow on the ground when she has just had a lovely run along the cliff path. However, two sunny days thaw the yard after the three months' freeze (-5°c to -14°c at night – and once, famously, -20°c in Caersws, according to Derek, the weatherman on the telly, who has become a friend this winter). A hundred years of compaction of said yard are undone in a trice, as the permafrost melts, loosening every particle in the top 30 centimetres so that a quagmire ensues.

They find themselves actually relieved when the temperature plummets and it freezes again, making it possible once more to venture out into the yard in slippers – albeit very carefully. This, the retired lady has decided, is the only advantage of sustained sub-zero living. To add insult, it is now snowing again. The lambs are due in less than a week. They are down to the last half-bale of hay and are feeding the pregnant ewes on calf-mix, which was all that the agriman had left in his warehouse last week. The tenuous nature of human existence is starting to dawn on the retired couple.

There is a kerfuffle at the front door, with much knocking and banging of the cat flap. The cat is trying to enter with a large, dead rabbit. Now, Pedro the dog, when he catches a baby rabbit, brings it in alive, tail wagging (the dog's). He pops it down in front of the retired lady, bewildered and spiky with dog-lick (the rabbit). He will then nose it towards her with that pleading, can-we-keep-it look on his quizzically inclined face. The cat has never shared his sentimentality for baby things. She takes her kill into the bread oven, from which emanate alternately sounds of growling, crunching and that cross between a purr and a gnaw that cats make when something is really delicious. The retired lady thinks of Noah and of the dove returning to the Ark with an olive sprig. She wonders if the cat's first rabbit of the season is a foretoken of fecundity to come – a harbinger of spring.

Outside, the falling snow swirls, dusting the frozen ground with icing sugar.

Kevin, the vanishing electrician, has materialised like the Cheshire cat in *Alice in Wonderland*. This is what he does: he appears when needed and does the minimum, whatever is critical so as not to impede the renovation process, then dematerialises with just an empty mug and a few crumbs to mark his passing.

Today he is not needed but has news. His son is driving for a local haulier and has gone to East Anglia for a load of hay.

Telephone numbers are exchanged. The retired lady feels like an insider trader. She goes to the phone by the computer to place her order. Meanwhile, the retired gentleman sets about removing the scrap iron that he has been collecting from the trailer. It is super-cooled.

'Twenty-five pounds a bale. Ten o'clock tomorrow', the retired lady announces when her husband comes in to defrost.

'Twenty-five pounds!'

'That's the bad news: they've only got big bales, but they are square and not round, about ten by six foot. He'll load it; we'll just have to get it off this end. Can we cope?'

'What do you think?' This remark is rhetorical. Ever since they first met, the retired lady, then anything but retired, has been setting him impossible tasks. 'Labours of bloody Hercules', he mumbles as he goes to look for the foot pump for the trailer tyres.

The retired gentleman is not in the least surprised to find that it is raining the next morning. The quagmire has returned and the west wind is blowing the rain almost horizontal. They don their waterproofs, find the tarpaulins and set off to find the Holy Grail – the last bale of hay in Wales.

The front-end loader carefully lowers the huge bale onto the little trailer, which sinks into the mud of the haulier's own personal quagmire. The trailer creaks and assumes an oblique posture, the bale resting on its triangular super-structure. It overhangs precariously and probably illegally in all directions. They cover it as quickly as they can with their trusty tarpaulin, the one that kept them dry all the previous winter. The haulier, having accurately assessed the situation and having a pronounced social conscience, insists on securing the load himself using miraculous haulier-knots. The couple watch, transfixed, trying to take in the way he does them and remember. The retired lady takes the twenty-five pounds to the back door to pay the haulier's wife. In the porch she finds a large, ginger tomcat with muddy feet. She strokes him as he expresses the injustice of his situation – shut out of the house all winter.

'Well, you're muddy and I expect you spray and make horrible smells and anyway you've got a jo …'

'Yes!' says the haulier's wife opening the door.

'I was just talking to your …' She looks down; the cat is gone. She feels foolish and holds out the money. 'Twenty-five pounds for hay.'

Before they set off, the retired lady checks that there are no trailing ropes or loops of baler twine with which to lasso cyclists. Being a woman who not infrequently hooks herself on door knobs, she is acutely aware of this danger.

'Oh do get in – I've done all that!' protests the retired gentleman. 'Just watch the load.' And off they wobble up the track. As she looks back at the hazardously balanced load, she notices, in the window of the haulier's house, sitting on the window sill, tucked behind the curtain and probably over a radiator – a large, ginger cat.

Number-one-son, who is staying for a few days, is up and about when they return. His girlfriend has returned to bed. She is not feeling well and one look at the weather was enough. She is a Londoner with a penchant for expensive and very glamorous shoes. Number-one-son doesn't like the idea of his aged father wrestling the giant bale after the dramatic cardiac events of his last visit. He feels obliged to volunteer to help the retired lady to unload. The rain has stopped.

They heave and strain, consider inserting rollers, a car jack, levers and winching it from the main cross-member of the barn roof (both agree it will collapse).

'What we need is an A-frame', says Number-one-son.

'My God! You sound just like your father. What we need is a carving knife.' The retired lady fetches her biggest, best knife and they proceed to cut the bail into slices (a very domestic solution), and pile the slices in the barn. Meanwhile, Pedro the dog has become convinced that there are rats under the pallets on which they are piling the hay. His nose is buried in the hay, sniffing professionally while digging with his front legs, occasionally lifting his head to sneeze. Hay is flying in all directions. They ignore him.

This single industrial-sized bale, once unpacked and man-handled, fills their humble barn almost to its tin roof (which leaks). Without being told, Number-one-son gets the tarpaulin and throws it over the stack. They weigh down the edges with timber. The retired lady sighs with relief as they admire their achievement – a bright blue, plastic covered mountain of hay, safely stored and just enough, perhaps, to tide them over until the grass grows

'Where's the dog?'

Hearing himself addressed, a bulge in the blue haystack bounces up and down and yelps. Timber is hurriedly moved, the tarpaulin lifted and dog extracted.

Now cats and dogs within the same household, contrary to popular myth, frequently work together as a team. They may not like each other very much, and may often snap and snarl at each other, but woe betide the stray dog that tries to chase the family cat. The family dog will see it off and chase it all the way back to the village. In return, the cat will render services to the dog. She will jump, shelf by shelf, to the very top of the wobbly Welsh dresser to topple over a defrosting chicken that has been put up there, out of reach of the dog. The retired couple's cat works in tandem with their dog. He is not allowed on the beds but sleeps upstairs. Soon after dawn he will descend the wooden steps to the kitchen door where he lifts the latch with his nose, releasing the cat from her nocturnal incarceration. The little female cat, named Ripley by the children because of her likeness to a popular alien-bashing heroine, always wakes with a fearful hunger. The retired lady is beginning to think that she may have a problem with an overactive thyroid gland. She is skinny and always ravenous. She demands food incessantly and, if ignored, will go straight out and kill something, eating until she vomits – in fact she is a bulimic cat. The dog cleans up the remains of her kills. This is another of the bonds that unites them.

Having let the cat out, the dog returns to his basket and the cat sets about her morning routine of getting the couple up. When young, the guileless kitten would sit on the pillow and tap the lady's face repeatedly with her paw, initially with claws furled but progressing to claws-out. This would result in the kitten becoming airborne with associated imitation engine noises. Once the process had been repeated several times, everyone was awake and the retired lady would proceed downstairs to reinforce this feline behaviour by feeding the cat.

In her old age the cat is much cleverer. She nuzzles the lady with her cold nose in a way so affectionate that it discourages cat-flinging but nudges towards wakefulness. If this fails, the cat has developed a very sophisticated alternative.

116

You know how bargees used to power their barges through tunnels in the days before engines, by lying on their backs on the barge roof, with their feet on the roof of the tunnel and walking themselves through? – the cat does this under the bed. She lies on her back and paddles herself round and round on the polished floor with her clawed feet propelling her, as they hook and tear at the underside of the mattress. The noise generated by this particular activity has a dramatic effect on the dog, touching his brain in some primitive way and producing the highest level of canine arousal. He will do anything to make the cat stop. He will not fit under the bed so runs back and forth around it barking, often having to jump over it, regardless of the occupants, to get to the other side more quickly. There is domestic pandemonium until everyone gets up and goes down for a cup of tea. But first (can you guess?) the retired lady feeds the cat.

On other mornings – if perhaps the retired gentleman, who does not feed the cat, is downstairs with the dog, and any amount of nuzzling has failed to rouse the retired lady – the cat resorts to air-attack. She jumps to the window sill, then to the top of the tallboy next to the couple's bed. From here she launches herself onto the chest of the sleeping lady. This always works.

However, today they are not awoken by any of this. They are jettisoned into sudden queasy wakefulness by the sound of screaming. Vixen? No, it sounds more like someone being murdered in their guest-room. They grab dressing gowns and run barefoot to investigate. The first clue is trodden on at the bottom of the stairs. It is cold and squidgy, like a rat's gall bladder. This is the reason they have been allowed to lie in – although, in their panic, they do not realise it at the time.

A large rodent, disturbed by the dog the previous afternoon during the stowing of the hay, has already made a substantial breakfast for the cat. As the couple fling wide the door to the kitchen of their little guest annex they find Number-one-son's girlfriend, ashen and slouched, fanning herself with her hand. Her boyfriend is offering water. She is breathing heavily but has stopped sobbing.

She mumbles incoherently about her foot and is waving her bare right foot about in some distress ... Cramp? No, Number-one-son indicates, with a nod of his head, the object on the floor by their bedroom door. Covered by a tea towel, only the very tip of a scaly tail is visible. The retired gentleman removes the large, deceased rat, carefully keeping it covered by the tea towel. The retired lady tries, without a great deal of conviction, to explain that when a cat leaves a kill by your door it means the cat really likes you ...

'And I'm sure that it was dead before you trod on it.' It does not help, so she slips away into the yard with her husband.

'Two rats in one night – bloody good cat that!' says the retired gentleman.

17

Sabrina?

THE days are lengthening, snowdrops have appeared in the glade, the purple tips of the silver birch are swelling with promise, the sap is rising and the retired lady notices a change in her husband. He stands in the yard gazing at the hillside in a strange, distracted way. He stops in the truck on the road to Y Fan to have a look at their neighbour's new digger – six-ton and yellow, with a very long reach. He looks long and hard at it. That evening he is on the internet. He says that it is really time that they got on with the track. He is browsing excavator websites with an interest the intensity of which she has previously only seen in Iolo's two-year-old grandson when he showed her his tractor catalogue. She has lost, she knows, any economic argument, though not yet even formulated. Still she goes through the motions – like a government consultation. She asks if it might not be better to hire a digger as required, to avoid unnecessary capital expenditure. He counters with the well-maintained second-hand value of same, especially with the state of the pound and the demand in emerging economies ... He had thought this through. Might it not be more sensible to get a contractor with his own machine ... and experience? He doesn't say, 'Where's the fun in that?' Or, 'What's the challenge?' He has worked out that a contractor (i.e. Maldwyn, down the road with his JCB) will always be busy doing bigger jobs when the conditions are right AND ... He continues with his well-thought-out argument, and the retired lady glazes over and capitulates in her own mind – she nods, acknowledging each point, one by one. She is reminded of the friend who has decided to leave her husband and family for a young lover and has rationalised the biggest mistake of her life completely and absolutely.

Digger, when she arrives, is not particularly glamorous. Her paint, though once brilliant orange, is now chipped and weather worn. Her panels are dented from years of careless ditching on a country estate. She has a long reach and choice of three buckets. Her contoured safety glass panel at the front of the cab was smashed long ago and her door is missing – all expensive to replace, making her a bloody good buy. She can still pack an amazing punch ... once started! And she can hold her head up afterwards (that means her hydraulics are good). The retired gentleman, sitting on her torn, damp seat is spinning round at an alarming rate as the yard fills with choking white diesel exhaust. The iron bucket on the digger's extended arm is whizzing around a vertical axis which passes through the retired gentleman, a grin now extending right around his spinning head. His wife wonders how far a retired cricketer could bat a round female object with a six-ton digger

– she moves further out of range.

As the digger-dealer leaves with the ink on the cheque still wet, the retired gentleman runs Digger up and down the track, checking the efficiency of the metal caterpillar tracks – they do churn up the mud a bit.

'She'll go into the wettest of ground. I think we should have a go at a pond before we start the track, just to get my eye in', shouts the retired gentleman from his cab.

Next morning, much earlier than usual, the retired gentleman is storming around the house looking for a piece of cigarette packet with a number on it. It has been moved.

'It was on the coffee table when the children were here', he shouts at no one in particular.

'Why not look him up in the book. You do know his name, don't you?' says no one in particular. 'It'll be on the invoice anyway.'

When the invoice is located, the digger-dealer's number is on it, but the aura of incipient crisis continues. There are a number of phone calls after each of which the retired gentleman rushes out into the yard to try something different – but Digger remains silent.

At eleven o'clock the digger-dealer has returned. A few seconds later the yard resonates to the sound of a waking Hitachi EX60, coughing, then spluttering – then running quite smoothly. Calm returns, if a little sheepishly. The retired lady does not ask what the problem was.

Whatever the problem was, it recurs. The switch incriminated in the first episode is now definitely switched on but, next day, Digger is stubbornly silent. Her new owner, reluctant to call back digger-dealer and have him start her effortlessly in seconds, perseveres. He twiddles and fiddles, checks levels and tightens nuts, and sticks his electrical screwdriver where Digger had never been tested before. Maldwyn calls in, unable to resist the beckoning of an albeit motionless hydraulic arm. He stands scratching his head.

'You need Tom. He's in his eighties but he's a tidy mechanic – got a real feel for it.'

Later in the day, Tom stands in Maldwyn's place, his baseball cap pushed back scratching his head, his little white van standing by, full of tools, sockets and spanners of every conceivable size and system.

'That's it – it's got to be that solenoid, but I think we can bypass it.' He disappears into the back of the van. Two minutes later, there is a coughing and a spluttering, a cloud of acrid white smoke and a cheer. Lifelong friendships are forged on less. And that is how it will probably be. This afternoon Tom also diagnoses the problem with the Cushman's back wheel, giving it several more years of troubled life. He removes the crucial bush which is preventing the camper-van side door from closing. After tea the retired gentleman disappears with Tom to see a man about an axle. When he returns he's got that little-boy-tractor-catalogue look back in his eye.

'This chap Tom knows, Mr Brownley, has got a metal lathe and a milling machine. He can do the most amazing work and he's going to make us a new keyway for the Cushman just from a block of metal. He's nearly ninety. Tom's over eighty but Mr Brownley calls him son!' Still chuckling, the retired gentleman goes out into the yard to turn over the digger engine one more time before it gets dark.

The pond is to be where the track crosses an area of upland bog by means of a causeway. The bog presently drains through this causeway in a large earthenware pipe – a culvert. The causeway – part-natural, part-enhanced (probably many years ago) – already looks like a dam. All that is required is a little digging-out above it, and there it is: a five-metre by six-metre pond, fed by three tiny tributaries of the River Severn (Hafren in these parts) – little streams originating from springs further up the land, then collecting water from the hillside.

Sabrina is the Roman Goddess whose job it is to guard the waters of the Severn. The Romans left in the fourth century AD, but Sabrina was somehow left behind (possibly she was troublesome then). Before starting this project the retired couple are pretty confident that they do not need a licence from Welsh Water or even permission from the Welsh Government (Rural Payments, Wales). They have unfortunately overlooked Sabrina.

Today they are looking at the great pit that they have created, dug a metre-and-a-half deep at its maximum, down to the bedrock. Today the water is still draining out through the culvert. The retired lady is puddling blue clay into the gaps around the plastic pipe that they have inserted to extend the culvert, her wellies working deeper and deeper into the mud until her husband has to extract her with a great squelch. He is standing on the dam wielding a red-and-white striped pole – the sort they use along mountain roads to gauge the depth of snow. He has the air of a surveyor.

Today heavy rain is forecast and they are going to insert the bung! They are still at an experimental stage so will need to remove it again later. To this end it is tied to the end of a washing line, for ease of extraction. This will obviate the need for a diver (the retired lady is grateful for this). Diving into a mountain pool, to retrieve a valuable item for her love, does not hold the romantic allure that it might once have done, and she is no longer really built for mud-wrestling.

The bung, brass and rubber, tightened by a central screw, is inserted and tightened. The rope is attached and draped across the bottom of the empty pond with its free end coiled on the bank. It is spitting and the retired couple stand on the dam, hand in hand, watching the great thunder clouds gather over Plynlimon.

Next morning, with great excitement, they stride through the wind and rain to view the pond: already half-full. This microclimate is amazing – the rainfall unbelievable. They are reminded of the tales of confounded engineers and meteorologists when the Clywedog reservoir was filled. The following day water will be spewing from the overflow pipes.

Not so! Next day they rush to view their engineering masterpiece and the balloon is burst. The pond is empty and the sounds of this little part of Wales have returned to normal: the gurgling of the culvert, the mew of the buzzards above. The bung has been removed!

It is nowhere to be found. Torches are brought and shone up and down the culvert. Every contortion is made to lower eyes to the appropriate level. The retired lady stands in the pond with her back to the culvert and looks though her legs as her husband shines the torch. There is no bung. There is no rope. They probe and then they track the stream right down to the house. The bung – £29.99 from Bunners in Montgomery – is no more.

Mud smears the banks of the outflow stream and the tall grasses at its edge lie listless. The story of Amos Jenkins having had three sheep washed away further down the valley is in fact untrue – that's Wales for you.

Sabrina?

Suspicion abounds. Who, or what, would do such a thing? Enquiry is made, to the delight of the drinkers at the Green Dragon (cf. Amos Jenkins' sheep). Acquisitive foxes and clumsy badgers are evoked, a jealous beaver recently released into the wild with a DEFRA grant – everyone knew that would be a disaster.

Sabrina? Who's to say. But when the council interfered with her flow to rebuild the bridge by Amos Jenkins' farm, no sooner had the concrete hardened than a storm blew up and a great tree fell, smashing into the bridge and blocking it with sheer pique. It could have killed a man.

Eventually a modified and improved bung is reinserted into the plug hole of the new pond. It has side-arms bolted on. CCTV is considered, but in the end they tie the new rope to a tree and withdraw to await the working of the rain. The following weekend the couple have visitors and the retired lady troops them all up to view the dam. The pond, to her surprise and delight, is full, with water splashing from the overflows. They stand and admire it for as long as they can bear, then throw sticks for Pedro, who is normally an agile and well-coordinated hound, unlikely to trip or tangle himself in a sturdy and highly visible fluorescent rope with a yelp and an irritated tug …

Great bubbles rise from the pond plug-hole. All are temporarily transfixed …

Then, as one, they rush to the far side of the dam to see the tidal wave, and to wonder at the speed with which a domestic dog of more than average intelligence can empty a woodland lake.

18

Living the Dream

S PRING is tantalisingly late in 2010. In the Trannon Valley, Mid-Wales, the snow had started well before Christmas and lasted until March; and when the thaw eventually comes the fields are brown – the grass looks dead. The fields around the house where the sheep have been all winter, for ease of feeding and supervision, are heavily fouled by three months' excrement, carefully preserved by the sub-zero temperatures. The retired couple, new to farming in this Alpine spring, watch their little flock of eight pregnant ewes in trepidation. Two years ago they started with ten. One died of infection after lambing in the first year, and one dropped dead for no apparent reason in the previous summer having lambed successfully. The percentages are all too easy to calculate and now they face another lambing season, still woefully inexperienced. Have they made a terrible mistake?

On the thirteenth of March the retired lady ventures out

at first light, her sleep pierced by the very first tweet of the dawn chorus. At the first sound of movement Aby, last year's cade lamb, calls from the field, out of sight above the house. This alerts the pregnant ewes in their field, who run to the cratch (a roofed sheep feeder) in hope of food – all, that is, but one.

She is alone under the hedge at the top of the field, where the first low rays of pale sunshine light up the dewy grass which steams a little in the chill morning air. It is definitely a little milder. The lady nevertheless dashes in for a coat and her box of paraphernalia.

'I think we're off!' she shouts to the retired gentleman.

'What?'

The retired lady, with her dressing-gown tucked into her waterproof trousers, steams up the hill – but she is learning: she doesn't walk directly to the ewe, but past her, up to the corner of the field, where she doubles back behind the remains of the old hedge, and perches herself on a horizontal tree trunk and watches.

The ewe is calling with the unmistakable voice of lambing, a gentle bubbly sound. She is standing beneath the hazel hedge and is sniffing the ground. In the leaf litter in a nest of leaves, unknown to its mother, the retired lady sees a flash of white – a new-born lamb. She wants to rush forward with her clean white towel and grab the lamb, clear its mouth of membrane, blow into its nostrils and dry it, but she holds back. There is a bleat – the lamb is breathing and answering its mother's call. The ewe sniffs along the ground towards it, her tongue tasting the ground, darting like a serpent's.

Scent, sound and taste draw the ewe to its lamb (as it can on the darkest night) and she licks its bleating muzzle, which rises in response. The breeze rustles the leafless hazel and the catkins dance. The ewe's flashing tongue works over the lamb which is already struggling to its feet and trying to pull itself towards its mother's belly. The back legs, which do not work too well, raise up its hind quarters which teeter, wobble and topple. The lamb rolls onto its back. Its mother licks its abdomen which is conveniently exposed. This process is repeated, and on each occasion the hind legs get a little more confident. Now the lamb has fallen under its standing mother, it sniffs its mother's hoof, its lips walk up the mother's leg, steadying its head, drawn by heat and scent, and bingo! It fixes on its mother's teat. Its tail wriggles, a message of triumph to its mother. She licks the wriggling tail. Above, a million wriggling catkins broadcast the same message.

Clean and fed, the lamb, now in control of all its limbs, curls up and goes to sleep. A moment later the mother turns and sniffs the ground beneath her tail. She turns again and again and gives her mumsical call. A balloon of liquor trapped in membrane is enlarging from beneath her tail. There is a slippery sound and a thud; the second lamb is born, smaller but livelier than the first.

A magpie bounces up the hill in huge, wing-assisted jumps to where the lambs were born, though now they are settled further up the hedge in the lee of their mother. It has been hanging around since the day before. They know when lambs will be born. Now it is pecking at the afterbirth on the ground. There is a flurry in the hedge from which, emerging at enormous speed, flies a buzzard. Diving to achieve such speed and bending its trajectory at the last moment to whistle through the hedge, it grabs the placenta and flaps its great wings, coasting above the ground like a bomber, membranes trailing, and is gone.

So, notwithstanding air attack, this is how hardy Welsh Mountain Sheep, lambing out, are supposed to behave – and this year most comply, watched obsessively by the retired couple. This is fortunate, for there is an aspect of sheep farming that is not as easy as it looks. There are men who the retired couple have watched; big powerful chaps whose families have farmed for as far back as anyone can remember, who can stroll into a pen of sheep and just pick one up and sit it on its bottom to cut its toe nails or whatever. The sheep sense their aura and comply instantly. Not so when a retired person approaches them for a bit of pedicure. These hardy, lively, hill breeds will climb over and under each other in a shifting woolly maelstrom, getting themselves covered in muddy footprints. If a retired person does not succeed in grabbing one, it pulls them round and round the pen, to emerge bedraggled and covered in sheep shit. All this assumes that they have been lured into the pen in the first place. It's not difficult to lure them in with expensive ovine treats. It has taken only a couple of years for them to train the humans to bring them a bucket of something yummy every time they want to interact with them. They will come running – except, of course, if they are ill or in labour, when they really need to be caught.

Today, the last of the eight, the largest (and they are beginning to think she may have triplets), remains stubbornly pregnant, growing vast as she soulfully watches the gang of lambs cavorting around their proud mothers. All the lambs are healthy, all born just after dawn, with the whole day to toughen up and dry before another cruelly frosty night.

This evening, at the wrong end of the day, the big ewe at last shows signs of labour. With a heavy frost forecast, the retired couple decide to get her in, and the circus begins. That is not all that is wrong: she has suddenly developed a very unpleasant and ominous odour, obvious from 50 yards away. The retired lady remembers a woman who died after an illegal abortion, way back in her student days. The retired gentleman also recognises the smell of death.

They know what to do: they must get hold of her during a contraction, then steer her to the barn. After three or four circuits of the paddock they pause to collect hurdles from another part of the farm (not for her to jump over, but to contain her). There is another intermission to remove those sheep they don't want to catch but who keep giving themselves up and getting in the way. It is dark when she eventually completely outruns them (they are not in the first flush of youth) and gets down by the stream where they eventually corner her in the water. What a disaster – two elderly, misguided, cold, wet humans, in a mountain stream in the pitch black with a huge, sopping wet and very sick ewe, incidentally getting bigger by the minute – a very bad sign where sheep are concerned.

They can't shift her onto the bank; neither can they help her where she is. In desperation the retired gentleman (did I mention he had a couple of coronaries last summer?) runs up the long, steep bank to the house and gets the truck, which he parks on the bank with its headlights trained on the scene. Not only is it hopeless, it can now be seen to be hopeless. He phones a friend, one of those strapping chaps with the aura. Meanwhile, the retired lady braces herself against the bank in 30 centimetres of fast-flowing icy water and hangs on to the ewe, chatting to her inanely.

Quicker than an NHS ambulance, Gareth is there, dragged

from his own farm at the busiest time of year to manhandle a sodden, dying ewe onto dry land and deliver three large, macerated and long-dead lambs while trying not to breath the volumes of foul gas which accompany them in great belching boluses. As he works he says, 'Don't beat yourselves up …'

The previous day he'd lost four lambs: three to the fox and one apparently laid on by its mother. 'That's the way it is.' Worst of all, one of his new heifers (he only has a few cattle) – one that he has lavished care on all winter – lost her calf and then died.

The retired lady is holding the ewe's head, whispering encouragement, and as the last lamb is extracted the ewe gives a great sigh, and dies.

19

Without Words

THE retired lady thinks a lot about words. She expends a lot of energy in selecting just the right one. She frequently interrogates her husband as if he is an interactive thesaurus, to find the most appropriate and specific word for her innermost thoughts.

'What do you call a man who stabs you in the back?' she asks as she stirs her pan.

'Treacherous? Traitor?'

'Got it in one … You are clever. Treacherous!' she says with satisfaction as she pours the custard.

'Shark infested?' asks her husband.

'No, just sticking.'

Words escape her more and more. She has aspirations to be a writer but can spend 20 minutes searching for just one word. She knows that abstract thought is possible without words when the word in question eludes her. She thinks a lot about communicating without words. She read somewhere that the spoken word delivered by telephone contains one eighth of the meaning of the same words delivered face-to-face. She is inclined to believe this. So what is the point?

She visualises her meticulously crafted sentence read aloud by a stranger who, with a sideways glance and a narrowing of the eyes, imparts seven times the impact and changes the meaning utterly.

At this moment their dog appears. He sits to attention just beside the cooker. He has something to say. He looks into her eyes with his own big brown ones, then flicks a glance at the back door.

'I know it's time, Pedro … Just let me finish making the pudding.'

With the trifle safely in the fridge they go out to feed the sheep. The dog bounds ahead to a nearby ewe and lambs. They don't panic but move promptly out of his way. It is a simple case of mistaken identity. The wind is in the wrong direction – she is the wrong ewe. They do not dignify this dog with a scatter or a regroup or a stamp of the feet. They can smell him. They know him and just move out of his way, as one might step aside from something slightly offensive. Another ewe – the right one – runs to meet him. She butts him affectionately and he licks her face: it is Aby. Her own lamb, a well-grown ram lamb, has followed her down the hill but now stands at a little distance looking embarrassed. He has never been bottle fed; he knows he is a sheep.

It's all in the scent, thinks the retired lady; we lose so much to make room for all these words. She remembers asking her daughter, when she was two or three years old, whose was the scarf hanging in the hall. The little girl had run over to it, pulled the end of it down to her nose, sniffed it and answered with authority.

The retired lady fills her bucket with ewe nuts and lays a line along the field. The hungry ewes jostle, always with one running around the outside of the group, like musical chairs, looking for an opening. As it finds a gap, it displaces another from the end, which runs around in turn. The retired lady thinks of the swinging balls of that executive toy that demonstrates Newton's first law of motion – elementary, she thinks.

As the ewe nuts dwindle, entropy ensues and twenty ewes mill about looking for their lambs. There is a frenzy of distraught baaing, answered by the panic-stricken lambs. Remember, all sheep look alike – even to sheep. They recognise each other by scent and call, by the nuances and timbre of that single syllable.

As they sort themselves out the retired lady notices that one of the ewes has her ears at a very peculiar angle. Now, when the retired lady was a little girl, her mother and her elder sisters would excuse themselves from involvement in her plans by virtue of headaches or the curse. She wished then that they could have an indicator on their heads. She would imagine them with a glass tube protruding from the tops of their crania; its red marker, like a thermometer, creeping up in exact proportion to her sisters' or mother's absolute and objective discomfort. This system, she would explain to God, would be very much fairer, and discourage neurosis and hypochondriasis. Everyone would know exactly how bad one felt. Unfortunately, as with so many of the retired lady's ideas, God had rejected it.

However, it was with great delight that, later in life, the retired lady discovered that he had instituted a prototype in sheep. When a sheep is happy, healthy and alert, its ears, according to Gareth's analogue clock face (and this is worth repeating) are disposed at five to one. If bored or slightly peaky they will drop to ten to two. At a quarter to three there is cause for concern; antibiotics are probably indicated. Ears below the equator indicate incipient demise, and asymmetry is a very bad sign indeed. This particular ewe's ears say twenty-five past three, although she is grazing, blissfully ignorant of her own parlous state of health or deep depression.

The retired lady tells her husband, who comes to look. She rings a friend who, with one eighth of his true feelings (he was in the bath), advises a wait-and-see approach.

The retired lady waits and sees. Early next morning the ears, whichever way you look at them, have completely collapsed, lifeless, moulded listlessly to the ewe's head. As she runs they bounce passively and apathetically with absolutely no will of their own. The retired lady observes the ewe from every side. The ewe becomes self-conscious and edgy. She pauses in her grazing to return the retired lady's anxious gaze. It is obvious, if you look very carefully, that she is chewing with less enthusiasm than on the previous day.

The retired lady tells her husband to get dressed and phones the vet. Despite perceiving only one eighth of her anxiety, the vet suggests that they bring her down. There then ensues a three-quarter-hour chase.

'She seems nippy enough!' says the retired gentleman as they pursue the ewe who now has the air of a French Foreign Legionnaire, her ears flapping out behind her like a kepi as she gallops across the field. The retired lady thinks about stress hormones, adrenaline and corticosteroids released by illness for flight or fight. She thinks of the importance to prey species of not letting-on to a predator that you are about to peg out. She thinks of this again as they finally corner the ewe in the pen, when suddenly she goes all limp and they have to lift her into the trailer.

On the way to the vets the retired lady thinks about insurance and trailer regulations; of chains to prevent separation in the event of linkage failure; of the fact that, technically, this is a stolen trailer, as their neighbour was out when they borrowed it. She starts to voice all these concerns to her husband.

'Shut up. We're doing it, aren't we?'

So many words, she thinks, and abstract ideas that I have to juggle with. Men with their warrior past are so much more instinctive. After all, you can't stop and have it out when you are in the middle of a battle.

The vet looks puzzled. She takes the ewe's temperature: it is very high. She asks if the ewe has been running about.

'Just a bit!' they agree. The ewe seems much stressed and has crackles in her lungs. She has pneumonia – worse on the right. The retired lady knew it: her right ear went down first. She knew there was something wrong.

'I'm going to give her an injection that will make her better,' says the vet emphatically (perhaps a little too emphatically, thinks the retired lady). 'It is not allowed out. I mean this drug has to be given by a vet. The truth is that it's rapidly fatal to humans if injected accidentally. Presumably vets are expendable!' The retired lady wonders if all this hype is to enhance the placebo effect of the drug – and for whose benefit, hers or the sheep's? She looks questioningly at the ewe who returns her quizzical gaze.

20

Left-Handed Challenge

THIS year, more than any other, everything they do on the farm seems to be decided by the weather – by the great looming thunder clouds. You would think, had you lived in Mid-Wales for some years, that you knew about rain; that you had experienced all varieties of precipitation, from the invisible exudation that soaks the fern-clad branches of the oaks in the dell to the driven vertical bars of water that sweep down the valleys, bending the trees and misting the ground, drumming the roof and confounding the newsreaders on the television, who stutter and freeze and stammer and disappear – their signal washed from the ether.

The rain here is not just something that keeps you indoors, something the garden needs. It is a force of nature and it transforms the land into a rushing, gurgling landscape of waterfalls. Roads flow and the ground seeps and glugs and tinkles from hidden gullies and cisterns.

In 2012 they say the Jet Stream has slipped, bringing all the moisture that evaporates from the disappearing ice cap down over the British Isles in a devastating deluge. Even in Wales, which drains well and is used to heavy rain, there are flash floods. After a sunny fortnight in March it rains until September. Once or twice in August the clouds part – just enough to reveal the heat wave above, before the weatherman gags and freezes, obliterated by yet another advancing front of Celtic monsoon.

The previous winter had been a wet one, with pools gathering under the sward so that it floated, spurting if you stabbed it (a trick witches used to do to demonstrate their power). In parts the path felt like walking on a quilted bed, a water bed. The ground around the retired couple's new cratch was a quagmire, a lake, 20 centimetres deep, of chocolate butter icing, quick mud that grabbed and sucked at wellington boots.

The worse the conditions are on a hill-farm, they are learning, the greater the need to walk the fields to extract their charges from wet and potentially premature graves – stuck in bogs and hooked with their heads in fences, as they look for a bit of extra grazing, or wound in bramble where their long winter fleeces hold them fast.

Finding them is only the start. Sheep will always prefer to travel away from intervention. Thus, as the lady pulls, the sheep, perceiving danger behind it, pushes itself with all its might and four-leg-drive into the fence, bog or gorse thicket.

The retired lady is engaged in a breech delivery; trying to extract a large woolly behind from the clutches of a fence when, in desperation, she rips the black, knitted hat from her own head and crams it on the sheep's, pulling it well down over his eyes. This is inspired: sheep no longer sees lady behind, instantly is compliant. She extends its neck, unhooks its little horns and out it pops, still in its black hat pulled over one eye. It does a lap of honour, which astounds the rest of the flock who do not recognise him in disguise. Thenceforth the retired lady carries a black fabric photographic bag for this purpose (very good light excluding properties – no peeping through the weave) in addition to the wire cutters and the little roll of wire (for repairs before she loses the hole). They are the weight of her responsibility.

The sheep need feeding twice a day and during lambing, which is surprisingly good. The lambs plop onto the wet ground, so that when the retired gentleman sounds the alarm from his position behind the binoculars in the bedroom his wife shoots up the field with a nice warm bath-towel to dry the poor little chap before the wind renders him hypothermic. Welsh farmers do this, the lady is convinced, in secret, as it is not considered manly.

All this observation, cautious care and the incessant interrogation of the neighbouring farmers is paying off. This year their 26 breeding ewes produce 40 lambs and the tally remains at 40 – well, 39¾ if you count the one that fell off the bridge and has a withered leg (not a wither – that is something else).

Despite the poor weather, when the grass does decide to grow it overdoes it, and the sheep almost disappear up to their wet tummies in wet grass. There are now 75 sheep gnawing at and fouling the fields around the old farmhouse, which looks on, an elder in this land, with the beginnings of foreboding.

The wet conditions make it a bumper year for all the nematodes and flukes and parasitic creepy-crawlies that live in the bowels of sheep, and a very bad year for their hosts. Ironically, this is just the time when the sheep need drenching (which is the technical term for the administration of worming medicine). But this has to be done, or if the sheep have to be immunised or gathered in for any other purpose it is more and more of a physical ordeal for the couple whose combined age is now 133 (still youngsters in hill-farming terms, but lacking the experience and systems which are usually developed in youth).

There has been a lot of gathering-in because of the orf. Orf is a pox virus causing what is known as 'thistle prickle' (sounds innocent enough). The retired lady had reprimanded the first lamb that developed it for fighting – it had a bloody lip. The actual diagnosis came to her in a flash as her daughter, a surgeon, was about to poke the lesion with her bare finger. Orf is one of the 'zoonoses', the group of bugs that can cross the barrier between species. Remember how cow-pox used to infect dairy maids and protect them from the worst ravages of smallpox? Sheep farmers have nearly all suffered from the painful and highly contagious blister on a knuckle that is human orf. It confounds most doctors in towns but eventually gets better by itself. Whether it protects against smallpox the author could not say, but it would be nice if it did. Come germ-warfare-Armageddon, only those with a proper attitude to life would thus be spared.

So far they have had two or three mild cases in the lambs. The corners of their mouths become thickened and warty, giving them a wry smile. The retired couple discussed it with the vet when they took in the last poo sample, and are feeling relatively relaxed about it – probably not a very virulent strain. They ask about incubation period in humans and make calculations which terminate in the week preceding their middle daughter's wedding. The lady makes a mental note to buy gloves.

Today the retired gentleman is making a journey. He is driving to the East Midlands to see his dentist and to smile in the mirror of his latest granddaughter.

'Pills?'

'Check!'

'Mobile phone?'

'Check!'

'Glasses? Two pairs.'

'Check! And my wallet and the keys to Number-two-son's house, in case they are out. I'm going now.'

As the retired gentleman drives out of the yard, the telephone in the house rings. It is the vet. The faecal egg count shows 6,000 eggs per high power field. Now, the retired lady does not baulk at the idea of a high power field (their fields are decidedly low power); she knows exactly what it means and it is bad – very bad.

The lambs have been scouring for days (not scrubbing the wet fields with carbolic but having euphemistic diarrhoea – farmers can be very delicate). Rather than treating every exacerbation of this with another dose of wormer, the retired lady has been sending off stool samples and only treating when indicated. Treatment is now indicated, imperative even. The retired lady feels a wave of panic pass over her.

The only cure for panic is the burning of adrenaline. This is easily achieved by feverish activity. She and the dog – not a sheepdog but an enthusiastic amateur – manage to persuade the sheep into the smallest field on the farm, which is next to their makeshift pen. They are not hungry so this has to be achieved by running back and forth behind them at an exact right-angle to the way in which you want them to go. The dog understands this perfectly. Simple vectors are in his DNA. As the retired gentleman is absent, and the quad bike silent, the sheep do not realise that the management mean business. Even when the lady opens the gate and fills the trough with nuts they are relaxed and troop in for a feed. She slams the gate.

'Damn!' Two dawdlers are left outside, chewing at the hedge. She opens the gate to let them in and three others escape. She builds a pen within the pen, next to the gate which, itself, acts as the fourth side; she opens the gate and the five run in. Groups of sheep are like molecules of mercury that have strong bonds between them. They like to run into each other. She closes the gate and demolishes the little pen.

Now she sets about pressing them. Normally this is done by driving them into a narrow section which is four metres wide (actually, it is their lane). The couple then follow, each carrying a two-metre hurdle. This system is flawed when there is only one. The dog does his best, but not being allowed, like his professional counterpart, to growl, snarl, snap or even raise his lip in warning, the sheep jump over him and escape. There is only one way: the retired lady collects all the hurdles and some deconstructed bunk beds, another bed frame and several large sheets of rigid insulation material. She builds a fence across the large pen. The sheep run to one side of it – again like mercury. Within this new smaller pen she builds another fence, more substantial this time. The gas laws apply: the smaller the volume of a given number of sheep, the greater the pressure. She ties the hurdles firmly and lashes them into the hedge on one side, leaving the other side free with only a small gap through which half the sheep pass willingly, not wishing to be separated from their peers. By one o'clock, and by a continuous process of repeated bisection of the pen, she has the sheep firmly pressed in a small area so that they cannot run around and hurt themselves. Their flies are also pressed above, humming in an irritating swarm.

Now the real challenge begins. She grabs a ewe (they are tamer than the lambs and accustomed to being handled). It shies away from the drench gun. Sheep have a way of accepting the inevitable, but this ewe understands the odds. She and the lady are about the same weight, but the ewe has four legs, better traction and a better power-to-weight ratio. She tests this by dragging the retired lady twice around the pen. Her peers move to facilitate this and the significance does not escape them. It is easier than the ewe imagined due to the lubrication. It is amazing how much lubrication 75 sheep can produce under threat of a dose of medicine. The retired lady, glasses askew, decides to compromise. She will drench the lambs. The ewes agree; the lambs do not.

Catching them and holding them, drenching them and marking them, is only possible by throwing them (not literally); tipping them onto their bottoms in all the lubrication.

After four lambs, now bedraggled and almost completely khaki-coloured and with the lambs not looking much better, the retired lady admits defeat. She goes to telephone Iolo.

21

Round Two – Colditz

'WHAT you need is some sort of race,' says Iolo, 'and a roof wouldn't go amiss.' The rain is now drumming all around them and the retired lady visualises a huge, vaulted, ecclesiastical lych-gate straddling their entrance, which is where she has gathered the sheep. The monsoon rain is running down her waterproofs, washing off all the sheep ordure from her unsuccessful bid to worm the flock in the absence of her husband and right-hand man (the hand with the strength and co-ordination). 'When he gets home you want to get him to put you up a few telegraph poles and some corrugated.'

Just like that, she thinks. 'They are in a terrible mess', she says.

He looks at the dishevelled flock. Each one is looking at Iolo – suspiciously. They are strangely graffitied, covered in crude, blue hieroglyphs.

'What does a target on the rump mean?' he asks.

'It's not a target; it's an eye. I've only got red and blue markers and the red frightens me. I keep thinking they're bleeding, and they had so many blue spots already I had to think of a different way to mark them – those ones have got eczema around their eyes. I took a photo of it to the vets, and they treated it like a quiz, and one of them thought it was due to mites, so we treated one and I marked the rest to treat later if it works, and it has, a bit, but I haven't got the stuff yet.'

'And the blue tails?'

'That's orf. Do you want some rubber gloves?'

He laughs. He has been handling sheep with orf all his life.

'Bloody painful, mind you.'

'You've had it?'

'Doctor told me there was nothing to be done. I got it on my knuckle here, but I saw the vet. He said he wasn't allowed to give me anything but told me what to get from the chemist – one squirt and the pain went.'

They decide to do the lambs first and then separate them off. It is time they were weaned and it might stop them passing the nasty orf blisters from their mouths to the mother's teats. If they get mastitis they will have to be culled.

It goes relatively smoothly but they find a lot more have orf, and two or three are quite bad. They inject those against secondary infection. Then they let the lambs out into the little field below the house.

They start on the ewes, who have the decency to resist. This is not their retired gentleman; who does this chap think he is?

'We'll have to do them in groups or we won't know where we are', says Iolo. Subdivision – the retired lady can do that. She unlashes a hurdle from the fence. Bending down, the rim of her hat pours its contents over her face, which makes her jump. Iolo laughs.

In fives and sixes they worm the ewes. Iolo wields the drench gun while the lady watches the heaving, milling mass and tells him which ones he has already done. They are wormed without further graffiti.

'Lively!' he says, 'I don't know how you managed to get them in.'

The retired lady does not tell him but instantly feels very much better.

That night, after the lambs are separated from their mothers, the baaing is incessant.

Before bed the retired lady goes to check them. One young ewe is running back and forth by the gate screaming for her lamb. The lambs are all shouting back. The other ewes reply when they hear their own lambs but are spread around the field chewing the cud with a look of resignation. She thinks they are trying hard not to hear, and that is what she does when she goes to bed. She tries to think about her daughter's forthcoming wedding. It is muggy but she closes the double-glazed windows.

'That sounds near,' she says to the dog next morning. He looks out of the window and grumbles. She goes to look. Two lambs are in the yard having escaped from the field where, the previous night, she had separated them from their mothers.

She opens the gate of the field to let them back in. They are as distressed finding themselves separated from their peers as they are from missing their mums. They are heading back into their field when three others make a dash to join them, and they all run back into the yard.

The retired lady is not good in the mornings. The dog looks accusingly at her.

'Damn!' she says.

She again builds her little pen adjacent to the gate. The five squeeze in to be near their peers on the other side of the gate. Then she opens the gate and they file out to join the rest. There is no more leakage of these mercurial beasts. She closes the gate and the temporary pen collapses with a great clatter of metal and expletives.

'Everything alright?' shouts the hedge.

'No it isn't. We've finally had to wean the little bastards and they don't like it. Did they keep you awake?'

'No, no, yes. Don't worry about it.' Jeremy, their tolerant neighbour, steps out from the hedge. He is in an elegant maroon dressing gown, wellies and is hugging a large shot gun. 'Shooting your rabbits', he says, then leans back into the hedge and makes a loud ping. It is only an air rifle – a bunny lollops away.

Jeremy, still in his dressing gown, helps her check the fence. They find two places where the poles are wobbly having rotted at the base and where the lambs have inserted their noses and lifted, making a hole beneath big enough to wriggle through.

The lambs learned this trick from one of Rhodri's ewes, a notorious escapologist who, with her two lambs grown fat on the council's verges (the long acre), had called in earlier in the summer, but checked out again minutes before Rhodri arrived to collect them. In desperation, when he eventually did catch them for the umpteenth time, he took her and her lambs immediately to Welshpool Livestock Market (it happened to be the right day). He left them in a pen to be sold and they were sold. Rhodri got the money. But when the farmer who had paid the money returned to pick up his ewe with two lambs at foot, they had left – last seen walking along the verge of the B4382 towards Llanfihangel and the heather-topped hills where the ewe had spent her youth. But I digress.

Jeremy helps lash down the fence and they are just think-ing about a cup of coffee when there is a shout from the lane.

'There is a lamb out here!' It is Jeremy's wife. She spotted it from the bathroom window while cleaning her teeth.

'Can't be one of ours; we're just about secure – wait I'll count them.'

'It's covered in writing; I've never seen anybody else do that.'

'Whoops, I'm coming.'

'It went up thataway.'

'Why do they always go uphill?'

Jeremy gets his car and drives up the lane while the retired lady walks up the inside of the fence of the field where the mothers are. Sure enough, she can see the lamb between the fence and the hedge beyond, surveying the posts one by one to find a weakness. Its mother is baaing encouragement from her side.

The retired lady goes up, beyond the lamb, then walks down the fence shaking the wire as she goes, driving the lamb before her and also noting the wobbly posts. When it reaches the gate the lamb shoots out into the lane just as Jeremy reappears in the car; so the lamb turns downhill and runs down the lane until it sees Jeremy's wife, who has set up a road block and is explaining to a motorist the nature of the current crisis. The lamb stops. It looks down the lane, then up. The verges are almost vertical here and as high as a house. There is a strange, clomping, wheezy noise. It is the retired lady who has reached her terminal velocity by lengthening her stride as she hurtles down the lane towards the lamb. The lamb glances down at the car and up at the hurtling lady and makes a snap decision. It runs as fast as it can upwards: when stressed, mountain sheep always head uphill.

The lady grabs at a passing tree trunk and pulls up in a precipitate parabola, then stands, like a rugby prop, to face the lamb. 'Oh no you don't – you little bugger!'

She opens her arms to grab at the charging lamb. It aims to one side. She moves to that side. It veers to the other side. She fixes it with her eyes and moves to meet it. It jumps into the air. They crash heads. The lamb falls backwards. The lady grabs and does not let go. They roll on the tarmac, the lady's arms clamped around the lamb. 'Got you!'

On this wave of adrenaline, the lady carries the wriggling lamb – 15 kilograms of unwillingness – back to its own field, where it shakes off the humiliation with aplomb, trotting through its peers like a returned Colditz hero.

'I did it!' the lady says to her neighbour.

'You certainly did', says Jeremy's wife. 'Let me see your face. When is the wedding?'

'Two weeks.'

'You've got a bump – about the size of an egg.'

'Is the skin broken?'

'I don't think so, but you'll have a black eye. Yes, definitely a black eye – it'll match your hat!'

22

Dog Days

Dogs, as you know, are dogs. Forget the peanut butter sandwiches and peeled grapes that you toss them; they are carnivores and they are pack animals, albeit in your gang. They have ambitions and will be leader of the pack if you let them – all of them. They are not to be trusted – none of them. In fact, the most loveable pooch is probably the cleverest, the most manipulative and therefore the most dangerous.

Farmers understand this and love their dogs no less. Every one of them can tell you, with tears in his eyes, the story of the best dog he ever had, who he had to shoot because it overstepped the mark, had too much initiative, thought for itself, had its own agenda and killed a sheep.

There are folk stories of farmers/ knights returning home to find their wife/ children/ chickens dead and their dog bloodied. They kill the dog, only to discover it was injured in the fight to protect said wife/ children/ chickens from a wicked marauder/ wolf – or (in Wales) possibly the *gwylltraid cochion*, the wild red-haired men of the north.

Every dog owner in a country area lives with this narrative. The retired couple are no exception.

Pedro – the best dog the retired couple have ever had – is running up the dingle ahead of the humans. It is autumn and the sun is just peeping over the hill, lighting up the golden hazel that hide in the green wood. The oak is the last to turn, and their leaves mottle the path with dancing light that catches the bright orange rowan berries scattered there, and the purple splatter from birds gorged on wimberries. Pedro holds his head high and struts ahead and above and full of confidence along the ridge, which is all that remains of the ancient hedge that skirted the path. Two of the grown-up children have come up for the weekend and he is showing off. On the breeze drifting down the valley are dog noises, and had the family following been less engaged in their conversation they might have noticed that it was not the usual calling of one farm dog to another across the valley, or the shout of a bitch in a barn wanting her breakfast and to be let out to run her pups around the yard. This was more of a hound sound and it makes Pedro prick his ears and sniff the air. This is his territory. But still the family chat and laugh. It's a good job one of us has his wits about him when the master's not here, thinks Pedro, who quickens his pace, widening the gap between himself and his feckless charges.

Then there is urgent barking.

'Where's the dog?'

'Christ! Pedro! Pedro!'

The dingle is a deep gorge at this point, with large trees

clinging to the steep banks of moss and leaf litter. Many trees have fallen and lie, their roots in the air, haphazardly obstructing movement. The stream descends steeply through this landscape in a series of falls and deep swirling pools. There are boulders heaped along the sides in towers and precipices, and the whole valley curves to the right and up and out of sight.

The barking, which is definitely Pedro, is from higher up, around the bend. It is a call for back-up, but the family are transfixed. They stand looking up at the pinnacle of precariously-piled rocks on the far side of the stream, their eyes riveted to the blood: red blood, glowing in the shadow of the vale, every drop piercing their eyes and awaking all that is primitive. It is smeared on a flat area on the far bank and has been dripped – a string of red lights – up the rocky pile where, bedraggled and bloodied, there stands a sheep, unsteadily at the pinnacle.

Their neighbour's wife, who is with them on the walk, runs ahead, up the path in the direction of the barking. She is the only one to heed Pedro's call. She scales a fallen trunk and disappears, still shouting for the dog.

The family see her go and turn back to the sheep – it has gone. They scramble down to get a better view: there she is in the water. She has fallen and been washed down the falls. Her head is just above the surface of a pool and she is struggling for her life. The retired lady is first at the water's edge having slid there, out of control. She eases herself into the water which comes halfway up her chest. Her feet slide on the rocks beneath but she manages to get behind the floundering sheep. Half-walking, half-swimming, she pushes it towards the bank. With its last strength its front legs paw at the bank and the lady heaves from behind. The skinny beast, in all that streaming, sodden wool, collapses on the bank.

'I've got him!' shouts the neighbour from high up the bank. She is holding on to a tree with one arm and holds a struggling dog with the other. 'Has anybody got a lead? He's hurt and very excited.'

'Take my belt', says the lady, 'I'm going to take my trousers off anyway.'

They examine the sheep. She has a number of puncture wounds around her neck but none are actively bleeding, and her right ear is bruised and crumpled. She is wet and exhausted and they decide that any further intervention will certainly kill her even if they could extract her from this deep gully.

Pedro has blood on his leg and is limping. The retired lady is flustered; she forces him into some shallow water and scrubs frantically at the blood on his leg making him yelp. She feels like Lady Macbeth. They all walk home in silence leaving the sheep in the hands of a more experienced shepherd.

The following day, without the dog, the lady ventures up the dingle. The retired gentleman accompanies her and their mood is grave. The lady leads them to the spot. 'I think this is it; it looks different ... Yes, look, there's where I slid ... Where is the sheep?'

'How would I know?' says the retired gentleman, 'but if it has been ripped to pieces by scavengers I think there would be more signs. You've seen the mess they make with a pigeon, and it wouldn't be easy to carry it away, otherwise it would be tucked up in our barn.' They walk back downstream, looking at every inch of the brook. They find a white sheep skull and, further down, the remains of a rotted fleece but nothing new.

When they get home Pedro is lying on the mat licking his leg. He wags his tail but they look away.

When their children have gone they have the conversation.

'I don't think there was time for him to attack the sheep, and it was on the other side of the stream. And he wasn't interested in her when we'd got her on the bank. He wanted to get away back up to where we'd heard the barking … and that's another point – the barking: it was never coming from the bank where the blood was.'

'You know how fast he can move; you saw him kill the rabbit on Van Hill. It was over in the blink of an eye.'

'But he didn't bark then, and then he was as pleased as punch with himself – it wasn't like that yesterday', the counsel for the defence continues. 'Yesterday he was barking like he does if he thinks there's an intruder, when he hears a fox. He was bothered. He wasn't pleased with himself; he wasn't even looking guilty.'

'Come on – if you can look guilty then you can be devious. This argument is getting out of hand. The truth of the matter is that dogs will be dogs. We both know he thinks he knows best and it's a constant battle of wills. It shouldn't be like that. He has to know who is boss all the time or he can't live in the country, and we already know that he can't live in the town. We have got to have him under control every second; it only takes a second. At the moment I'm not sure that's the case, otherwise we wouldn't be having this conversation.'

The next day is Monday and the vet is open. The retired couple take their dog, Pedro, the best dog either of them has ever had. The vet says, 'He is very highly strung.' The lady bridles but says nothing. 'Which one of you will hold him?' They both do and he gradually slumps in their arms and his tail lies still on the table.

That evening they return to the vets. They collect his lead from the receptionist and go through to the back where the pens are, to collect him. A vet-nurse is attending to a caged cat. She is talking to someone, telling them all about what she is doing. The listener is sitting next to the cage, very upright and frowning with concentration; his head is on one side. When he sees the retired couple he wags his tail but does not leave his post: Pedro is learning about vet-nursing. His paw is bandaged in bright blue plastic crepe and two little stitches are in the skin of his empty scrotum. He is unaware of the latter.

'When he was asleep', the vet says, 'we had a good look at that leg. It is a bite, almost certainly canine and very large.'

'Thank God!' says the retired gentleman. The vet looks puzzled.

In the early spring of the following year, the retired lady is carrying a bucket of ewe nuts up to the yearlings in the top pasture. The dog is running ahead then stopping and tearing back, threatening to knock her over then swerving at the last minute, going round her back to walk proudly to heel for a few steps. 'There's a good boy.' Then he repeats the whole sequence. 'You are a tease.' Then he picks up a stick and puts it just in front of her. She bends as if to pick it up. He snatches it and runs off. They play this two or three times until the lady says, 'Leave it!' He drops the stick at her feet and she puts down her bucket and slings the stick right over the stream to the bank on the other side.

On that bank, beyond their boundary fence, in the stock-excluded woodland, she sees a strange thing. Standing motionless by a holly thicket looking straight at her is a bedraggled, one-eared sheep, grey against a patch of melting snow. 'Stay, Pedro!' she says, and the dog stands. She looks back and the sheep is gone.

23

Prejudice and the Eternal Conundrum

G ARETH and his friend Roli are loading the retired gentleman's beloved digger onto a low loader. It is going to
help drain Gareth's top bog.

Gareth doesn't hold with ecological clap-trap and schemes
dreamed up by graduates who don't own a pair of waterproof
trousers. He doesn't claim subsidy for bat boxes and barn
owl schemes, but he farms sustainably (that's a good word)
in a place where it's tough to make a living, and he does it by
keeping down his overheads and maximising his productivity
by good husbandry, hard work and hardy stock. Oh, and his
wife goes out to work. Part of the quality of his farming is in
the teamwork.

Since the Iron Age, farmers have survived in this part
of Wales by helping each other. The local museum has early
photographs of shearing, when farmers teamed up and moved
from farm to farm to shear each other's stock and to enjoy

each other's company and convivial hospitality. Huge joints of mutton were roasted in bread ovens, with enamel washing-up bowls of creamy, eggy, rice pudding.

In the Elan valley, not far away, this enterprise (the shearing) used to involve up to 100 tenant farmers and labourers who swarmed over the hills, from farm to farm in a well-fed and boisterous crowd, leaving a trail of dazed and chilly sheep and empty larders.

The retired couple first met Gareth when he came to help the chaps who were doing their preliminary fencing. The retired lady interrogated him in her normal way but the interview did not go well.

'It's a very isolated profession, farming, isn't it?' she says rhetorically, thinking of the long, lonely hours spent in the cabs of combine harvesters by the farmers of her previous acquaintance.

'No!' says Gareth.

'I've read that there is a high incidence of mental health problems in the farming community, largely undiagnosed?'

'No, I don't think so.'

'And alcoholism – there certainly was where we lived before.'

'And what do you suppose drove them to drink?' The others present prick up their ears.

'Oh, I think it was the isolation that got them. I could tell because whenever we met they would keep me talking for ages – starved of company they were.'

'That's interesting but I must get on with your fencing – you've kept me here talking far too long – I expect it's the isolation.' The lady smiles uncertainly and the fencers chuckle.

'That young man has teeth', says the retired lady to her husband that evening.

'Met your match, have you? Certainly has got something about him.'

'I think I must have touched a nerve.'

'Perhaps you were just wrong', says the retired gentleman. His wife wonders if she has caused offence. A few weeks later Gareth calls in for no particular reason. They have a cup of tea and Gareth tells her that he has never seen a kitchen with so many cobwebs, that she is over-feeding her ewes and that he prefers milk chocolate on his biscuits.

Henceforth, when the retired couple shop, they buy one packet of plain chocolate biscuits and one of milk – but the milk always seem to disappear first.

'You want a young, healthy flock'. This is what Gareth repeatedly tells the retired couple.

'But ...'

There are, it seems, no buts. Old sheep eat more. That's only because they have produced so many lambs. Their milk is weak. Is that a fact? Older ewes are easier to handle. They have lambed before. You know their idiosyncrasies. The old ones will give you trouble, eventually. The retired gentleman knows both sides of the argument and sees the sense in what Gareth says.

'It's a bit like wives!' he says. This does not help.

'We can't get rid of all the old ewes just because they have lambed four times. It just isn't fair; they haven't done anything wrong', says his wife.

'Do you want them to get worn out and ill? She-who-must-be-nameless is ever so thin.'

163

'She'll be okay when I've fed her up.'

'You see! They eat more!'

She does see, and their little farm does need to be a real business, and it does need to be done properly.

'I'll go through the stock book and grade them all. We can cull the ones with problems: 47 and 48 are getting very skinny and number two's facial dermatitis is no better and it's costing a fortune in vet's bills and she looks such a sight …'

So, after a selection process to rival that for a chief executive of a nationalised industry or the provider of the main line east coast rail service, nine ewes are ready for market.

They plan an early start but the retired lady insists on scrubbing out the borrowed trailer with disinfectant and changing her clothes several times before they leave. The ewes do their part by refusing to enter the trailer, which reeks of chlorine, and they eventually set off at eleven o'clock. If we are too late, she thinks, we will just have to bring them home; perhaps we could rent some more land. She does not say this.

The extraordinary thing about the large livestock market is the way it works. It is like a beehive. Everyone is doing what they do, as if directed by invisible pheromones exuded by the market manager at the centre of the hive. There are no arrows, no signs, no directions. No one wears a uniform – not even a discreet badge or corporate boots – and no one tells anyone what to do. Hundreds of trucks and trailers move in and out and disgorge their cargoes smoothly and quietly. The sheep are hefted to the hills; they know where they can go and what to do. The farmers, perhaps, are hefted to the market by generations of familiarity, even though this is the new market. It is all very puzzling.

The retired lady jumps out of the truck and looks for someone to ask. There are acres of covered pens made of gates that can open in both directions and can be constituted in an infinite number of ways, to open up vistas or to close off whole sections. Farmers move effortlessly through this maze, opening and shutting gates as they go. At this moment they have all gone.

Eventually she accosts a man walking back to the car park. He points further down the building. She beckons furiously to the retired gentleman. He backs the trailer into a space between two others; they are empty. She rushes off to find someone. In the distance there is the unmistakable sound of an auction, and around the sound she sees a huge herd of farmers, and as the auctioneer moves rapidly from lot to lot, so the herd follows. It is moving inexorably closer. She struggles through gate after gate; each seems to fasten in a different way. She looks up and sees the smiling face of a neighbour – thank God.

'Yes, these are cull ewes. You can leave them here.'

She hurdles her way back to the trailer, where her husband is rolling a cigarette. This only calms him. The gates won't open; they are welded. The entry bays to the market along the zigzag perimeter are on every other zigzag. The retired gentleman had carefully backed into the space between two bays. They look at the maze.

'Jam every other day', says the lady, 'but never today.'

The retired gentleman moves way down the line of parked empty trucks and backs into the very last bay. The gates of this one do open and the sheep can disembark. The lady sets about making a route across the maze to the pens of the cull ewe area. She starts opening and shutting gates to move her reluctant flock. A well-dressed elderly man crosses her path. She enlists his assistance, which he gives willingly and with great alacrity. She has to push '47' along with her leg. 'What's wrong with her?' asks the man.

'Nothing, she's just tame and she doesn't want to go.' Once they are in their pen she thanks the man and goes to find someone to tell.

'Wait a minute', says the man, getting a tiny piece of paper from his pocket, 'who are you?' She gives her name and address, which he writes on his little chit and it is all done.

As they talk about the domino league with their neighbour, she can see her ewes watching her; so can the retired gentleman. 'We'd better go', he says.

At the next domino match the neighbour admits that, after thirty years of farming, leaving the old ewes at market is the hardest thing. No one hangs around a cull ewe sale; all are quiet and in a rush to get home.

The conundrum is that the older or the sicker an animal is the more care you have lavished upon it and the more it trusts you, so the more reluctant you are to part with it. Perhaps that is why God is supposed to love sinners so much, thinks the retired lady.

24

Festive Fish – Big Ones in Small Streams

'Lovely it was: tender as anything and juicy. I haven't tasted anything like it for years.'

'And it came out of the River Trannon, you say? Our River Trannon?' The retired lady is cross-examining Big Roni in the pub. He is still salivating after the best and biggest salmon he's ever eaten. 'And it was a Christmas present? Now, who would give you that?'

'I couldn't tell you that – illegal, see, at this time of the year.'

'Did he have to disguise himself as a woman, like they used to do, to avoid identification? Have we got a Rebecca in our midst?'

'I couldn't say.'

'You mean you'd have to kill me!'

'That's about it.'

'How exciting – no wonder it was so delicious.'

'But I didn't think there had been salmon in the Trannon in living memory. Even old Dai Tickle only ever talks about trout, and that was when he was a child. I've never even seen a trout in the Trannon – except for the one we put in; the one Little Lawry caught with a bent pin in the reservoir and brought to us to restock our stream. That's Mair's eldest grandson. He's only nine and wants to be a farmer. He's very keen. Always wears a flat cap and waterproof trousers. He puts them on as soon as he gets home from school.'

'I know – don't they live in London?'

'That's right: Hendon.'

'His grandad was a good farmer … Badger Faced.'

'That's not very kind!'

'He kept Badger Faced Welsh – fine flock. You'd better have another drink – you're not keeping up!'

'Better not, but thanks', says the retired lady, 'I've got some serious cooking to do.'

'That fish – too big for me. I've put the rest in pieces in the freezer. I'll bring you up a bit after Christmas.'

'That'll be lovely. You can help us eat it.'

The truth is that they have (although she does not tell) a big, juicy salmon of their own to share with their assorted grown-up children – who are, at this moment, returning from statutory Boxing Day exercise, bedraggled and mud-spattered, looking for something medicinal. Her husband is uncharacteristically willing to leave the warmth of the pub and the reassuring click of the dominoes. He has remembered that he has forgotten to put his whisky away at the back of the bread oven, safe in the care of the dark and the cobwebs.

Their salmon is not from the Trannon but from Morrison's

in Newtown where it was offered at a ridiculously reduced price to fecklessly late shoppers on Christmas Eve – Scottish. 'Lovely!' they all agree, 'tender as anything and juicy.' They hadn't tasted anything like it for years.

The best thing about Christmas in Mid-Wales is the singing: carols in Welsh and English in church and chapel – ecumenical, washed down with tea and cakes, when everyone brings a plate of something very special. There is a service called Plygain, which means matins (held in the evening!) Plygain is an open-mike night at the chapel – ecclesiastical karaoke but with an organ.

At Christmas services, children sing solos and family duets and no one is afraid to applaud their efforts. No-one goes home disappointed, as vicars and ministers-melodical ask, 'Has anyone a favourite hymn that we haven't sung yet?' The retired gentleman wonders if he can get away with *Oh Come All Ye Faithful* again if he asks for it in Welsh, but someone beats him to it and they sing *O Dewch Y Ffyddloniau* with great enthusiasm – and descants – and the old chapel expands with the sound of male voices raised in praise and anticipation of the miracle, and the gastronomy, to come.

That's the difference, the retired lady thinks: the Church of her childhood vibrated to the warble of 'conservative ladies at prayer'. In Wales, she feels the blast, the boom and the ricochet of men's voices as they lift the roof off its rafters with the might and skill of their combined exultation. They lift it high then lower it gently back into place – pianissimo. But after the last carol, after the last joyful crescendo, the roof is gone, and everyone goes to the vestry for tea.

The retired gentleman's domino team, the Green Dragon 'C' (newly formed and a 'social' team) has a Christmas party. It is halfway through the season and they have quite a lot in their kitty, so the local landlady (praise be upon her) makes them a wonderful buffet and they invite their wives and girlfriends (one or the other, not both) and children to join them for food, drink and friendly play – although, to men so focussed on their sport, this is difficult (no one likes to be whopped by their ten-year-old daughter in public). 'It's all in the dominoes', they say without conviction. Domino players believe this maxim only when they lose. When they win, a good player can always reduce the effect of a bad hand and a bad player can waste the advantage of a good one!

The retired gentleman fills his plate with beef sandwiches, coronation chicken baps, sausage rolls and chicken legs. 'Don't hold back!' his team-mates say.

'Don't worry!' says the landlady, 'I've catered for farmers' appetites!'

Someone shouts that the retired gentleman is a farmer. He looks pleased and adds a couple of profiteroles. Everyone laughs.

That night the retired couple come second in the knock-out.

The following week it is the regional open (well, the village open – but 32 people enter). All the great and the good of the domino scene are to attend: old campaigners, tomcats with torn ears from years of combat, men who have given their all to the game and those who have given up drink for the sake of their adding up and speedy division, doyens of probability and intuition.

The retired gentleman crawls into bed at 2.30 a.m. and his wife struggles to open one eye to view the Trannon Valley

Open Champion. He has beaten Big Roni in the final. Both are 'C'-team members. So euphoric are they for their team that they share the prize.

'I hope this won't make a difference to our position here', says the Open Champion to his wife.

'What do you mean?'

'Well it's bound to make a bit of a stir. Arwel said I was the first foreigner ever to win it – I'm not sure if he was joking.'

'Trannon Valley International Open Champion!' says the lady, who kisses her husband's furrowed brow and slips back to sleep.

Next day they drive into the market town for feed-blocks. Their way is blocked by Iolo's sheep surging up the valley for their scans. It is time for clever ewes, who have conceived twins, to get their mark and their extra rations. Iolo leans into the truck. 'Going to spend your winnings then?' he says.

'I didn't think you played, Iolo', says the lady.

'I don't. Never had the time, but you can't keep a thing like that to yourself. You'll have to watch your back. There's people here who take it all very seriously', he says, winking at the retired lady. 'Of course, they are shadows of their former selves.'

'You'll be paying cash today!' says the man at the feed store, 'heard you knocked out Merv in the first round. He was in this morning to buy a billhook – funny time of the year to buy a billhook.'

'What's a billhook?' asks a grandchild who has come for the ride.

'What we call a billhook is what you'd call a machete', says the man.

Next day it is the Merched Trannon party, when the ladies of the valley entertain their friends with children's party games and homemade crackers and cakes. Someone has brought some homemade wine and, what with that and the woolly hat game (a sort of musical chairs with hats), everyone is strangely dishevelled. Before they sit down for the spelling bee, which is always won by Anastasia (a retired, peripatetic Methodist minister undaunted by Welsh place names that leave her countrywomen screaming in despair), they will draw the raffle.

Now, when they came in, the retired gentleman noticed a rather fetching flat cap amongst the raffle prizes. It is of a blue tweed material. He tries it on and it is a perfect fit. On the strength of this they buy several strips of tickets. Now the excitement is rising. The gateau piped with chocolate rosettes is won by the large lady from the post office. The boxes of chocolates go next. The winners after that choose the bottles of wine – all three, one after the other. The bath oil and the calligraphy set (left-handed) go. All that remains now are the blue tweed hat and a rather attractive blue jug – the retired lady collects blue jugs.

'It's on the yellow: number 36! Melyn: tri-deg-chwech!'

'That's us!' The retired lady rises and edges her way towards the prize table by the door, through the sprawled revellers, the man pulling out the cork with his Swiss army penknife, the litter of screwed-up Christmas paper, discarded biscuit tins and fallen hats. She grabs the blue flat cap and hastens back to her seat, placing the hat on her husband's head in triumph.

'Thank you', he says quietly.

'Oi!' shouts an elderly man who is pointing at the retired gentleman, 'That's my hat! I left it on the table by the door. What's he doing with my hat?'

25

Hopeless and Three-Quarters

Twenty-six! All present and correct. The retired gentleman stands on the running boards of his quad bike in his new flat cap (bought by his wife in Llanidloes – she has the receipt) and stretches his injured back. Their top pasture, Troid-y-rhiw, is looking better than it has in any of the last seven years. Their new topper has really got to grips with the bracken – and without recourse to chemicals.

The grass is thick and green, albeit thicker and greener where the rain soaks down from next door's fertilised field, but they can't help that. This part of the farm is designated as 'no-input pasture'. Their new ecological stewardship scheme is more to do with preserving the character of the landscape than producing lamb, but that suits them.

They wonder who decides at which point in time the landscape should be frozen. Should it be a snapshot of picturesque Victorian hill-farms or should it be moorland with hefted flocks fending for themselves and collected in great round-ups once a year? The retired lady is inclined to think that if you really care about ecology you should forget the sheep altogether and reforest the whole area with a tangle of inaccessible deciduous woodland. She would reintroduce wolves and wild cats, wild boar, beavers and bears – but then she knows she's barmy. Mostly now, she and her husband think like farmers.

When they started, it crept up on them gradually. They felt like farmers when they counted their little flock every few days. Now they really look at their animals and they never miss a day. They walk around them all, get them up on their feet, check their gait for lameness, for the limp of foot-rot or the stiff-legged hobble of mastitis. They look at their faces – not just to see what they are thinking, but for signs of dermatitis or orf, and they never fail to check the disposition of the ears!

In a glance they take it all in, the individual's mood and their general condition. They can tell if they are hungry, cross, fed-up or frisky. They note their breathing for signs of fever, pneumonia and heat stress. They feel their backs, assess the fatness of their loins. They look for signs of parasites and fly strike, rubbing or itchy twitching, pilling of the fleece, soiling from scouring. They check their abdomens for signs of distension, and the lady sniffs the air for effluvium, the whiff of pathology; and she looks at the manure on the ground to see if they are getting enough to eat, for signs of infestation, for blood; are there still flies about? They collect samples.

Today they look magnificent, all 26 of this year's breeding ewes – even if Aby (the tame one) is still sulking about being separated from her last year's lamb. The retired lady has explained that it is only temporary – until the ram has served the older ewes. She fondled the lamb this morning in the field above the house and now she offers her hand for Aby to sniff, 'See … She's fine!'

'Are you coming?' shouts the retired gentleman, waiting by the gate. The lady runs down and clambers on to the back of the quad bike, being careful not to smear her husband with mud or kick his painful back as she swings her leg over the seat and settles behind him. The dog runs ahead.

It is the end of October, the very end of the shepherd's year. It is 'snowing' leaves, a blizzard of autumn's detritus in the peppery air. This year's crop of lambs has gone. Loading them into the trailer for market was what did for the retired gentleman's back. As he bent down to manhandle them up the ramp (woman-handling having failed) something clunked with excruciating pain and there he was stuck, bent double and howling.

All the fuss distracted the lambs or stimulated his wife enough for one final roar and lunge and up they went. Loaded – gate closed.

The retired lady could then see about unbending her husband and loading him, moaning softly, into the driver's seat of the truck. She cannot back a trailer; illness is unthinkable. This is why farmers go on forever. Their lives are constantly urged on by imperatives. There is no time for a paracetamol.

The lambs are sold. Those that go for breeding do reasonably well. The store lambs, sold for fattening elsewhere, fetch disappointing prices. The couple complain like real farmers.

That is where it stops though. They have kept five and three-quarters of this year's lambs.

Three-quarters is a special ewe lamb, six months old but

undersized and untagged, never expected to survive. They found her the day the retired gentleman announced that he would have to mend the bridge. He would have to mend it before one of those damn lambs gets its foot stuck in the crack. Three-quarters got her back leg stuck in the crack then fell off the footbridge over the stream and dangled by her foot until the retired gentleman came upon her by chance while helping Pedro find his missing ball. At first he thought she was dead but as he tried to free her trapped leg she looked at him and moaned. He lifted her back onto the bridge, then ran to get the crowbar and shouted to his wife. The lamb rallied and freed herself. As the lady got there she was pulling herself onto the bank, her hind quarters flattened and flaccid, like a bat on the ground.

'I think she's broken her back!'

'Damn! I was going to do the bridge today.'

'They can get spinal shock', says the lady. 'She's young and bendy; she might just have bruised her spinal cord.' They make a pen for the lamb in the shed and lie her on a bed of hay. 'It's always the brightest, liveliest and most inquisitive individuals that seem to come to grief', the retired lady says, thinking of Stoke Mandeville and of all the boisterous bikers and spirited horsewomen she'd met with spinal injuries.

'Bollocks!' says the retired gentleman, thinking of his own youth.

The lamb does recover, a little. Next day she is lying on her side and one back leg is moving, like a dreaming dog. They stand her up and she can bear weight on that leg, but topples over when she tries to walk; the other leg is paralysed. There is swelling and bruising on the inside of that thigh. They take her to the vet.

She is x-rayed and has not obviously broken anything; she might recover. That night she returns to the pen. Her mother, fortunately, has another lamb and cannot count, so does not call – so the lamb does not call very often either. She is not hungry. The lady has made her a hot drink and some biscuit. She is not keen on the baby's bottle thrust unceremoniously into her reflexively sucking mouth, but this is another imperative and the retired lady is not prepared to argue. Three-quarters quite likes the ewe nuts.

In a few days she is hopping around with the others – but only until the weather gets bad, which it is most of the summer. Then they find her cold and wet and caked with mud, wedged under the water bath in a puddle. The others have found shelter on higher ground but Three-quarters has got left behind. She is washed and dried and fed and goes back to her cosy barn.

They compromise: if the weather is good, Three-quarters stays with the sheep; when the weather is bad, they open the gate and she takes herself off to her place in the barn. Soon she can call to have the gate opened to get in or out. Usually she wants to come in.

That's fine, agrees everyone – you can keep her for a year then she can go into your freezer.

The retired lady has other plans. She believes in miracles and that the paralysed leg is definitely starting to carry a little weight and is starting to waggle slightly in time with walking. The nerve is gradually regrowing. If these months of paralysis have not distorted the shape of the pelvis she might still be good for breeding. The retired lady does not share these hopes with anyone apart from Three-quarters, who has very dark eyes and looks thoughtfully at the lady's face when she is talking. The large ulcer on her club-foot is not a problem at present. It has no feeling and is clean, washed every day in the wet grass. 'We'll cross that bridge when we have to.' When they do, just a few weeks later, Malci comes up with his rifle so that Three-quarters does not have to be stressed more than necessary.

Gareth is less approving of one of the other lambs that they have decided to keep: it is Aby's ewe lamb (she had twins this year). Its sibling was male so had to go – and it is small. The retired lady knows that, by this time next year, it will be just as big as the other four fine breeding ewe lambs that they are keeping, and she is probably right.

'It'll catch up.'

'Because it'll eat more!' says Gareth.

'I don't care!'

'Argh!'

It is All Souls' Day. Next week is Guy Faulkes, November the fifth, when the ram will come and the whole cycle will start again. Today the retired lady is mindful of ancestors – not hers particularly, but those who lived in the house before them, and in the hill-fort above them in the days when they milked the sap of birch trees for fertility and sorrow.

They are the people whose lives have touched their own, obliquely and indirectly, through this place, through the things they have seen and learned about the land, about their stock and about themselves. They too watch the hare cavorting along the skyline at twilight, see the sunlight through the trees, the rainbows on the hill, the rooks calling as they gather, like a swirling school of fish, in the pink dusk sky as they roost in the woods above the house. They have felt

178

the harshness of the weather and known the difficult decisions, those imperatives that keep one moving on. Though they have not faced starvation, nor lost a baby, nor known the aching, physical loneliness of isolation, they have learned just a little of what these ancestors knew. They have felt the bond between man and wife (struggling together with a seemingly impossible lambing or a seized and inaccessible nut and bolt). They know the bond between man and dog, between sheep and shepherd (that most biblical of relationships) and between man and his God – *Dew!* They have experienced the security of good neighbours and a full woodshed, friendship and the miracle, year after year, of new life. Most of all, they are connected to this place.

As the retired lady slips off the quad to fasten the gate, Pedro points for a moment, his tail straight out behind, his nose high, sniffing the air. 'What is it Ped?' and they hear a gunshot from the moor above the farm.

The dog is off (and remember: he is fox-coloured), bounding up the field towards the gunfire. 'Leave it! Pedro, leave it.' Now the dog is actually under the control of his nose, not his ears, and he knows something that the retired couple do not know.

'Leave it Pedro!' they both yell, and as he approaches the fence, in that tiny hesitation of intent which must occur even in dogs before they leap, he hears his master's voice booming, 'Leave it Pedro!'

He stops and looks over his shoulder at the couple standing by the quad bike, watching aghast.

The fox – a huge, dark, dog fox, almost black in this light, with a great flailing tail – is now aware of the dog, an old adversary, and only feet away on the far side of the fence.

He breaks his cover from the tangle of dead bracken between new and old fences where he is hiding from the huntsmen on the hill.

Now the couple see him. He jumps the old fence, swerves obliquely across the neighbour's steep field, toward the wooded dell and safety, his brush painting a great swathe on the ground.

The black fox escapes.